Living with a Handicap

The thalidomide tragedy has made many people aware, perhaps for the first time, of the problems of caring for children with physical disabilities. Indeed between three and six per cent of the world's population have some sort of disability, either congenital in origin (such as Spina Bifida and Cerebral Palsy), caused by road accidents, or the results of chronic disabilities such as arthritis.

For the disabled, the activities of daily living present severe problems. Even simple actions, such as rising from a chair or bed, may become extremely difficult. This book gives valuable information on the most up-to-date aids to mobility, such as walking aids, grab rails, wheelchairs and hoists. It also gives advice on personal care, from adaptations in clothing and food utensils to grooming and toilet activities, as well as suggestions for help in reading, writing and communication in general. It describes the range of hobbies and leisure activities which can be enjoyed by people with disabilities of all kinds.

This book will be of real practical value not only to patients but also to parents and relations who may have to care for disabled patients, as well as medical staff involved in their care. It has a special section on the disabled mother and the disabled housewife and gives solutions to some of their problems in looking after their children and their homes.

THE CARE AND WELFARE LIBRARY

Living with a Handicap

Philip Nichols

MA, DM, MRCP, DPhysMed.

Foreword by
Professor Henry Miller, MD, FRCP
Vice-Chancellor, University of Newcastle-upon-Tyne

with the assistance of:
Betty Hollings, MAOT
Betty Rostance, MAOT
Nancy Wright
Disabled Living Research Unit,
Nuffield Orthopaedic Centre,
Headington, Oxford

PRIORY PRESS LIMITED

The Care and Welfare Library

The Alcoholic and the Help he Needs Max M. Glatt, MD, FRCPsych., MRCP, DPM

Drugs: The Parents' Dilemma Alexander R. K. Mitchell, MB, ch.B, MRCPE, MRCPsych.

Schizophrenia Alexander R. K. Mitchell, MB, ch.B, MRCPE, MRCPsych.

Sex and the Love Relationship Faith Spicer, MB, BS, JP

VD Explained Roy Statham, MB, ch.B

The Care of the Aged Dennis Hyams, MB, BS, FRCP

The Child Under Stress Edna Oakeshott, ph.D

Student Health Philip Cauthery, MB, ch.B, DPH

I.Q.—150 Sydney Bridges, MA, MED., ph.D

Stress in Industry Josph L. Kearns, MB, BCh., MSC

Health in Middle Age Michael Green, MA, MB, BCh.

Children in Hospital Ann Hales-Tooke, MA

Healing Through Faith Christopher Woodward, MRCS, LRCP

The Baby's First Days James Partridge, MA, MRCP, BCh.

Sexual Variations John Randall, MD, FRCP

Depression: the Blue Plague C. A. H. Watts, OBE, MD

Care of the Dying Richard Lamerton, MRCS, LRCP

Aggression in Youth Roy Ridgway

The Slow-to-Learn James Ellis, MED.

When Father is Away The Rev. A. H. Denny

Allergies Douglas Blair Macaulay MD

SBN 85078 084 5 (Hardback)
Copyright © 1973 by Philip Nichols
First published in 1973 by
Priory Press Limited
101 Grays Inn Road London WC1
Made and printed in Great Britain by
The Garden City Press Limited
Letchworth, Hertfordshire SG6 1JS

Contents

We would like to acknowledge the help given by members of the nursing, occupational therapy and physiotherapy staff at Mary Marlborough Lodge, and the Information Service of Equipment for the Disabled.

The author and publishers wish to emphasize that all the characters in the case histories are fictitious.

Foreword

UNDER Nuffield patronage and influence the Oxford Hospitals have long enjoyed an enviable and well-deserved reputation in the fields of orthopaedics and rehabilitation, and Dr. Nichols worthily represents the Oxford school in one of its less central but most important activities. His book epitomizes a recent but very definite shift of emphasis in clinical medicine and surgery from the drama of acute illness and radical cure to the quantitatively much more important and certainly more exacting field of chronic illness and continuing care. Such a change of direction is evident in much that is written about medicine today, though it is as yet slow to influence medical education.

Dr. Nichols has written a remarkably comprehensive book, and it is difficult to think of any physician who will not find it of immediate practical value. The detail which he devotes to such difficult problems as dressing, shopping, toilet training, and mobility within and outside the home is most impressive. No detail from the installation of grab rails to the use of flexible drinking straws is ignored, and proprietary names of appliances and utensils are included. *Living with a Handicap* contains a wealth of clinical examples, a valuable reading list, and sources of further information including the addresses of relevant organizations. It brings together information which is otherwise available only from many different sources, and I believe it will enjoy wide readership not only within the medical and allied professions but also amongst social workers and patients and their families. It contains more material of real value to practising clinicians and to a large group of their patients than many more pretentious volumes.

Henry Miller

University of Newcastle-upon-Tyne, June 1973

Disability and Handicap

THERE are a very large number of people in this country who are physically disabled in some way or another. The exact number of disabled people is not accurately known, but from surveys made in several countries of the western world and Great Britain, it is clear that between three and six per cent of the population have a physical disability of some kind. These figures are, if anything, an underestimate of the real size of the problem, for so much depends upon the way the survey is carried out and the definitions which are used to determine disability.

There is a tendency to use the word to describe the more obvious conditions affecting the ability to use limbs, such as amputations, strokes or arthritis, but the more hidden disabilities, such as bronchitis and heart disease, often impose very severe physical limitations. In fact, the three words: Disability, Impairment and Handicap, are frequently used in a very similar fashion. Sometimes it is even difficult to distinguish why there should be any need to separate the meanings of these words; sometimes it is easy and sometimes it is difficult to see why one word should be used instead of another.

However, it is now generally accepted that an Impairment is the loss of part or all of a limb, or a limb, organ or body mechanism that is defective. So an "Impairment" is the actual medical condition that is wrong with a person. It may or may not respond to treatment.

"Disability" is the word now used to describe a loss or reduction of ability to "do things," or, to use a technical term, "the loss of functional ability." The third word, "Handicap," describes the disadvantage of having a disability or impairment, and the restriction which this imposes upon a person.

Thus, if a man involved in a road accident has his leg amputated, he has an "Impairment" (the loss of a leg). Because he has lost his leg he is unable to walk about and run as he used to. This is a functional disability, so he is "Disabled." If he is a young man and has been physically able to adjust to his impairment by returning to his old job, or by training for a new job; if he is able to drive his car—possibly with the controls adapted for operation by hand—he may be restricted to some extent by the loss of his leg, but he may not necessarily be handicapped. On the other hand, if he was employed as a steeplejack or an instructor in mountain climbing, then he may well find himself occupationally handicapped, for he would be unable to return to his former job. If he is a young man, possibly unmarried, he may find that the loss of his leg is a social handicap as it restricts his leisure activities. Among older people the commonest reason for amputation is a restricted blood supply to the leg. Such an impairment will be a greater handicap. It may be impossible to climb stairs or walk any distance outside the home because the other impairments caused by the faulty blood supply, such as breathlessness and general weakness, will be much more noticeable.

Handicap is different from both impairment and disability because many other factors are involved : the person's job, the place where he lives, whether other members of the family can help him, and whether he is in a financial position to overcome the practical problems imposed by his disability.

Thus, the "Impairment" is the disease, disorder or injury which a person suffers. The "Disability" is the loss of functional capability imposed upon him by the impairment; and the "Handicap" is the disadvantage he suffers in his own particular circumstances.

However one assesses physical disability, there are a number of medical conditions (impairments) which repeatedly occur as the commonest problems.

Common disorders causing physical disability
    Osteoarthritis
    Rheumatoid Arthritis
    Multiple Sclerosis (Disseminated Sclerosis)
    Hemiplegia (Stroke)
    Respiratory infections (Chronic bronchitis)
    Cerebral Palsy (Spastics)
    Paraplegia (paralysis of the lower half of the body)
    Tetraplegia (paralysis of all four limbs)
    Neurological disorders (Parkinson's disease etc.)
    Muscular disorders (Muscular dystrophy etc.)
    Amputation
    Accident (fractures etc.)
    Low back pain ("slipped disc" etc.)
    Cardiovascular disorders (coronary disease etc.)

Some conditions can be grouped in order of the age of onset of disability
Children :   Cerebral palsy
                Muscular dystrophy
                Spina bifida

	Still's disease (juvenile rheumatoid arthritis)
Young adults:	Spinal injury following accident
	(Tetraplegia, Paraplegia)
	Fractures
	Amputation
Middle Age:	Rheumatoid arthritis
	Multiple sclerosis
	Hemiplegia
Elderly:	Osteoarthritis
	Lower limb amputation
	Bronchitis

Cerebral Palsy: By far the largest group of physically disabled children in this country are those with Cerebral Palsy (Spastics). This is the term used to describe a group of non-progressive disorders of motor function, associated with brain disease or damage. These children may have partial paralysis or inco-ordination of voluntary movement as their major handicap. The brain damage does not necessarily mean that they are mentally handicapped.

Muscular Dystrophy: This is the name of a group of disorders characterized by a progressive weakening of the muscles. The commonest form of dystrophy is pseudo-hypertrophic muscular dystrophy which usually becomes apparent in early childhood (about three to four years of age). The child develops a wide based gait, an inability to run as fast as other children, a tendency to fall over, and tiredness. With the assistance of calipers and braces for the spine the child is able to continue walking for some years, but usually needs a wheelchair during adolescence. There are as many variations of this condition, each with its own pattern of weakness and natural history.

Spina Bifida: Spina Bifida is a term used to describe a range of deformities associated with incomplete development of the spinal column and the spinal cord. The deformities range from a relatively minor bony abnormality only noticed on X-ray, to the severe residual deformities associated with a severe meningomyelocele which means that part of the spinal cord is exposed when the child is born. This may be associated with severe bony abnormalities of the spine, or it may be a relatively minor defect.

In recent years, there have been great advances in treatment through early surgical closure of the defect, but it is not often possible to predict the likelihood of residual paralysis both of the legs and of the bowel and bladder. Severe spina bifida is often associated with hydrocephalus, which may also require surgical management to prevent the condition developing.

Still's Disease: Juvenile rheumatoid arthritis is relatively uncommon, but represents a potent source of severe disability to young adults. The disease appears in many ways, usually with fever and

13

inflammation of the joints. In more than half the patients the disease does not cause permanent disablement, but some are left with restricted joint movements, particularly in the hips, knees, elbows and small joints of the hands. In very severe cases, the spinal joints may also stiffen.

Paraplegia: Paraplegia means paralysis of the lower limbs. It is commonest as a consequence of spinal injury, usually a fracture or fracture dislocation at the lower end of the thoracic or upper lumbar spine. The most frequent cause is from road traffic accidents, but severe falls from a horse or a building are also common causes. Often the bowel and bladder are affected. Some disease processes, such as multiple sclerosis, may cause a similar condition, either in full or partially.

Tetraplegia: Modern high speed accidents, and some sporting accidents such as diving accidents, may cause a fracture or fracture dislocation of the neck. This may lead to paralysis, partial or complete, and includes the trunk and arms as well as the lower half of the body.

In both paraplegia and tetraplegia, muscle (motor) activities are affected and sensation is also lost or diminished. This means the affected person is very likely to develop damage to the skin from pressure and minor accidents which he cannot feel.

Fractures: Broken bones of various kinds, although probably one of the most numerous conditions requiring hospital treatment, luckily only contribute a small proportion of impairments leading to permanent disability. However, arthritis in one or more joints near a fracture occasionally occurs many years after the original injury, and almost invariably if the joint itself was damaged. In a few cases the fracture may damage the nerve with consequent paralysis.

Fractures of the femur (thigh) are relatively common in road accidents, particularly motor cycle accidents. These fractures may result in permanent impairment and disability, and represent a significant source of handicap in modern society.

Probably the most important injuries from the standpoint of long term handicap, are head injuries. The skull may or may not be fractured, but severe head injuries give rise to brain damage and are a potent source of long term disability and handicap.

Rheumatoid Arthritis: This is a common disease, affecting women more than men. The peak incidence occurs in middle-age and affects two to three per cent of the adult population of the western world. Although rheumatoid arthritis is a progressive disease with no known cure, it is often mild and self-limiting. There is much that can be done to reduce the effects of the disease. Correct medical management includes the use of medicines, proper rest, splintage, surgery to prevent joint deformity, and surgery to correct joint deformity if it occurs.

As age increases, degenerative changes take place in damaged joints and the elderly arthritic frequently presents a complex picture of rheumatoid arthritis and osteoarthritis (see below). Thus the late effects of the disease can be disabling, unless the patient remains under continual medical care.

Multiple Sclerosis (Disseminated Sclerosis) : By its very nature, this disease of the central nervous system is often not clearly diagnosed in the early stages. It is inconsistent in its progress, periods of deterioration alternating with times of improvement.

The effects of the condition are scattered (disseminated) through the nervous system and are also scattered through the life of the patient. Often it affects the eyes, causing attacks of double vision, and it may cause the speech to be slurred. Movements of the limbs may become inco-ordinated and there may be muscle spasms.

However, in many instances, there are periods of considerable remission of symptoms. Many of the patients develop a remarkably stoical and euphoric approach to their disability, which although often aggravating to their family and companions, may be a blessing to them personally.

Hemiplegia (Stroke) : Paralysis of one side of the body, temporarily or permanently, commonly occurs in the middle aged and elderly as a result of a blockage, temporary or progressive, in the arteries supplying the brain. It is one of the commonest of all disabilities but varies in its effects, depending upon the location and amount of brain function affected by the reduction of the arterial blood supply.

In severe cases, the patient may lose consciousness and die in the early stages. In others, the effects may be transient or with only minimal residual effect. In some instances, speech or sensation or sight are affected to a greater or lesser degree. The commonest problems are those of a severely affected arm with little real use, and a partially affected leg on the same side.

Osteoarthrosis : Osteoarthrosis (or Osteoarthritis) simply means wear and tear in a joint, and in more scientific terminology is defined as a degenerative condition occurring in middle-aged and elderly people. Many people develop some osteoarthrosis in one or more joints, and it is most likely to occur in joints that have been damaged by injury or disease. Thus a sportsman who has had many injuries to the knee joint is likely to develop osteoarthrosis of that joint.

It is the underlying condition which gives rise to so many of the common aches and pains we are all prone to : the screws, rheumatism, fibrositis, are some of the terms used to describe muscular pains deriving from underlying joint wear and tear. Although it is not a progressive disease, stiffness and pain in one or more

15

joints, most commonly the hips and knees, can be extremely painful and debilitating.

Some people are more prone to joint wear than others, and some people have a lower resistance to pain than others, consequently it is not possible to generalize about the relationship between joint damage and symptoms.

In recent years, severe osteoarthrosis of the larger weightbearing joints, the hips and knees, has been treated surgically. The trend now is towards replacing a severely damaged joint with an artificial one. This procedure was originally restricted to older people, with only one severely affected joint, but it has proved so successful that the treatment is being offered more frequently to a wider range of patients.

Lower limb amputations: Each year, about four to five thousand operations for amputation take place in the United Kingdom. The majority of these are necessary because of chronic circulatory disease, and are carried out on elderly people. Amputations following injury tend to occur in the younger age group, and the ratio of lower limb amputation to upper limb amputation is greater than ten to one.

The single amputation of a lower limb should not constitute a severe disability for a young person, but elderly people tend to have special problems since they are frequently weak and sometimes arthritic; but if they are given gentle and realistic care they can usually achieve a useful degree of independent living.

Chronic Bronchitis: This disease is highly prevalent in Great Britain and is characterized by persistent coughing and expectoration due to excessive secretion in the lungs. The two most important factors causing the disease in this country are atmospheric pollution and cigarette smoking.

Much can be done to prevent severe disability from bronchitis by giving up smoking, treating the overlying infection, helping to free the secretion with special inhalations, and training the patient in specialized breathing techniques to clear the mucous from his lungs. But there are still a very large number of chest invalids, and it is a potent source of loss of earning power in middle-aged men.

Handicap in the U.K.

In 1971, in conjunction with other departments, the Social Survey Division of the Office of Population Censuses and Surveys carried out a census of handicapped and impaired people in Great Britain, on behalf of the Department of Health and Social Security, the Scottish Home and Health Department and the Welsh Office. This census was only a sample survey, and was restricted to people over the age of sixteen living in private households, and therefore estimates must be on the low side. However, the survey indicated that there were about 150,000 very severely handicapped people needing special care, and 356,000 severely handicapped people needing considerable support. There were 616,000 who were appreciably handicapped and needing some support, and nearly two million who were physically impaired but who needed little or no support for their everyday living activities. The majority, nearly sixty per cent of the impaired, were elderly, and the greatest single cause of impairment (affecting 700,000 women and 200,000 men) was arthritis. But, as we have said before, impairment does not always result in a person being handicapped and the greater proportion of these people are able to carry out their usual everyday activities with only minor difficulties and discomfort.

Just over a third of the people of working age who have an appreciable handicap have retired prematurely, but half of them are working in ordinary employment, as are some of the severely handicapped.

The survey also showed that a high proportion of handicapped people are not on the Local Authority Register of substantially or permanently handicapped persons. Although this does not mean that they do not receive authority help, half the disabled population, and two thirds of those with an appreciable handicap, have no regular ongoing help from their local services.

The local authorities provide most of the support for the handicapped through their health services and the social services. After 1st April, 1974, the health services will be integrated for administrative purposes with local hospitals, but the social services of the local authority will probably be the most important co-ordinating link between the disabled person and the battery of facilities they may require. These will include home nursing, chiropody, home helps, meals on wheels, provision of telephones, holidays and many other amenities depending upon the authority and the person's needs.

Of course, many people with an impairment are able to live a full and active life without any special aids and equipment. Indeed, many of the hospital consultants who have most to do with such patients tend to spend more time advising them how to manage without such aids than prescribing them. This is the correct approach, for disability does not necessarily mean handicap. In some cases, contributory factors such as housing, transport, inability to make social contacts and finance may constitute the handicap.

Provision of aids for living with a disability should, ideally, be preceded by a full assessment of the disability by the doctor, therapists and technicians, so that a practical evaluation is made of the person's ability to use such aids. To obtain good results from any equipment, the user needs to understand the techniques involved in using it. If the person has a handicap he must learn not only the use for which the appliance was designed, but his own particular technique for using it in the most beneficial way. He may also have to learn that sometimes it is wiser to accept help for some activities, so that he has time for more rewarding tasks. For example, many people consider that the ability to walk a few steps is preferable to using a wheelchair, but for a large number of people, a chair provides the key to greater independence, both for getting out into the community and for coping more adequately at home.

Sometimes, people who need aids to help them with their daily living are overwhelmed by a collection of aids and equipment from well-meaning relatives and friends, which may be daunting in variety and complexity. Much more can be achieved by learning the necessary skills step by step. Altering a routine or using an aid may take time before advantages are apparent, but once achievement has been reached then it is easier to move on to the next step. It is just as important to plan a continuing programme of training in the home situation as it is in hospital.

It is known that a large proportion of the aids and equipment supplied by hospitals is not used by the patients when they return home. Often this is due to an unrealistic assessment of the domestic needs when viewed from the hospital situation. Unfortunately, there are few centres in this country which are specifically designed to evaluate the capabilities of severely disabled people, where they can try simple and sophisticated equipment, and receive training in its use. Many people who need help and advice rely on the local authority health and social services and the domiciliary occupational therapy service, who are usually in a better position to give a realistic assessment in the home situation.

The Chronically Sick and Disabled Persons Act, deliberately drew attention to the problems and voiced :

"... concern that these problems should be more widely known and studied," and urged "... that when priorities are settled, full weight is given to finding solutions."

Since the Act came into force, much has been done to extend the facilities and information available to disabled people, but much has still to be done.

The booklet *Help for Handicapped People*, which can be obtained from any social security office or local authority social services department, outlines many of the benefits which are available under the National Health Service and from the Department of Health and Social Security. Advice is given on doctor and hospital services; local authority health and social services; and how to obtain financial help. Special help is available for certain groups of disabled people, such as the poorly sighted, mentally ill, the deaf, and physically handicapped children and babies. Advice is also given on facilities for education and employment.

Additional services are also available from voluntary organizations such as the Spastics Society, the Muscular Dystrophy Group, the Arthritis and Rheumatism Council, the Chest and Heart Association, the Multiple Sclerosis Society, the British Red Cross, and many others, who provide an invaluable service with the advice they give on specific disabilities.

In London, the Disabled Living Foundation provides an Aids Centre and Information Service where professional workers, disabled people and their relatives can seek practical advice and demonstrations from one of the largest and most comprehensive display of aids for disabled people in the world. Some of the aids are specially designed, and others are ordinary household goods which have proved helpful in certain situations. None of the goods displayed are for sale, but information is given on sources of supply. Visits are arranged by appointment.

Another useful source of information is the Disablement Income Group which was founded in 1965 with the aims :

"Of securing for all disabled people a national disability income and an allowance for the extra expense of disablement; to co-operate with other bodies for the improvement of the economic and social position of disabled people and the chronic sick; and to promote research into the economic and social problems of disablement."

Branches of this organization exist in many of the larger towns in the United Kingdom, and a quarterly magazine is published providing information on incomes and government policy, together with articles written by disabled people.

The National Fund for research into Crippling Diseases sponsors a publication entitled *Equipment for the Disabled*, which is a series of booklets containing detailed particulars of aids and equipment currently available. The booklets are compiled and edited by members of the medical and remedial professions, and are primarily provided for the professional workers in the health services, but they are also available in some of the larger public libraries.

Although there are many sources of information and advice on aids and equipment for the physically handicapped, it should be stressed that the greatest care must be taken to ensure that any aid provided is the best and most suitable for the individual. Whenever possible, advice should be sought from medical personnel, the social services, or the domiciliary occupational theapy services, for the request for one aid may be the tip of the iceberg and with the full support of the social services, most people with a physical disability can be helped to live a more full and independent life.

2

Mobility in the Home

FOR the majority of disabled people, restriction of mobility is likely to be the most common handicap. There are many aids to mobility, ranging from a walking stick to an invalid powered tricycle.

Walking aids

A person with arthritis in a leg can use a walking stick or a single elbow crutch to relieve weight on the affected leg. However, better weight relief and balance can be achieved by using two supports, and great care should be taken to ensure that the height of these appliances is correct; a walking stick handle should be level with the hip joint when standing erect in shoes and a crutch handle should be level with the elbow when the arms are held at the side. The handle of the stick is important, and a straight one is frequently preferred to the traditional curved type. Many sticks and crutches have handles which are too small for a stiff hand to grip strongly, but these can be adapted with soft padding made of sorbo rubber or plastic foam so that they are more comfortable to use. Lightweight metal walking sticks with plastic moulded handles for either the left or the right hand are commercially available.

Many people with arthritis use a quadruped—a stick with four small legs. These are particularly suitable for anyone with poor balance. The three-legged variety are not as satisfactory, as they do not provide the same stability. A single quadruped is often the best aid for a person recovering from a stroke.

A walking frame is used by a number of people with severe disabilities. These frames have four legs, are very stable and give good support. When taking each step they are lifted and placed further ahead. Although the common walking frames are very light and many elderly and frail people find them an excellent aid, if the hands and arms are weak a walking frame with two small wheels on the front legs and with arm supports may be more useful. Such frames do take up space, and some people find them cumbersome, whereas others find them indispensable. Indeed, an ordinary tea trolley may well give enough support, although these

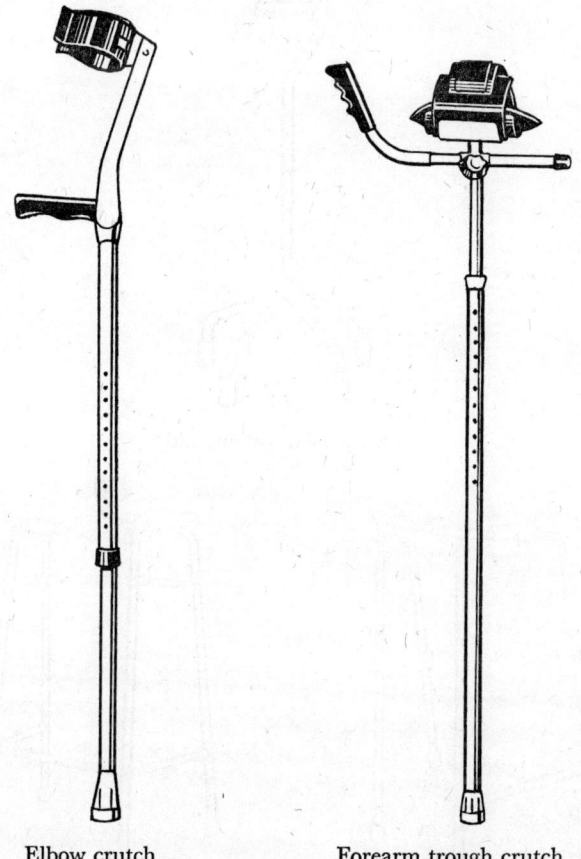

Elbow crutch   Forearm trough crutch

are apt to "run away." But it is possible to obtain a specially designed trolley with wheels that "brake" as soon as whoever is
pushing it leans upon it.

All sticks, quadrupeds and walking frames should be fitted with
large, renewable rubber ferrules, *which should be replaced as soon
as they become worn*, for they provide the necessary grip and
support on which the person using the aid relies. The ferrules of
a walking aid are like the tyres of a motor car, when they become
worn they are dangerous.

Bed

Although it may seem strange to discuss beds under a heading

21

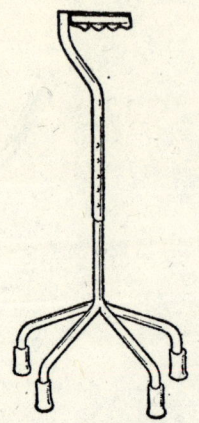

Quadruped walking aid

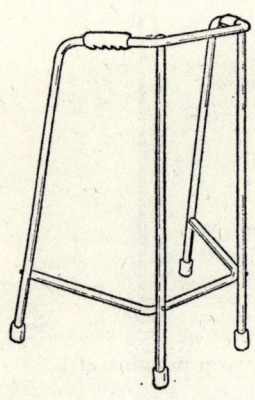

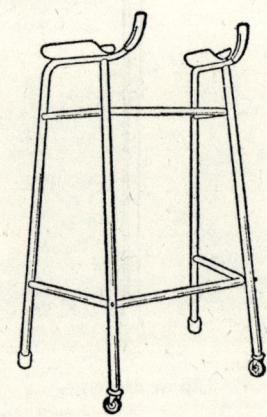

Standard walking frame   Walking frame with gutters for
arms, handgrips, and front wheels

of mobility, it is essential for the disabled person to be able to get
into and out of bed if he is not to become bed-bound.

The conventional low divan is unsuitable for some types of disability, and the more disabled the person the more unsuitable is
such a bed. For many people, the critical height is when the feet
just touch the floor while sitting on the edge of the bed; for
others the bed needs to be higher so that the buttocks just rest
on the edge of the bed when the person is standing. Some people
find that a well-sprung mattress will enable them to rise by

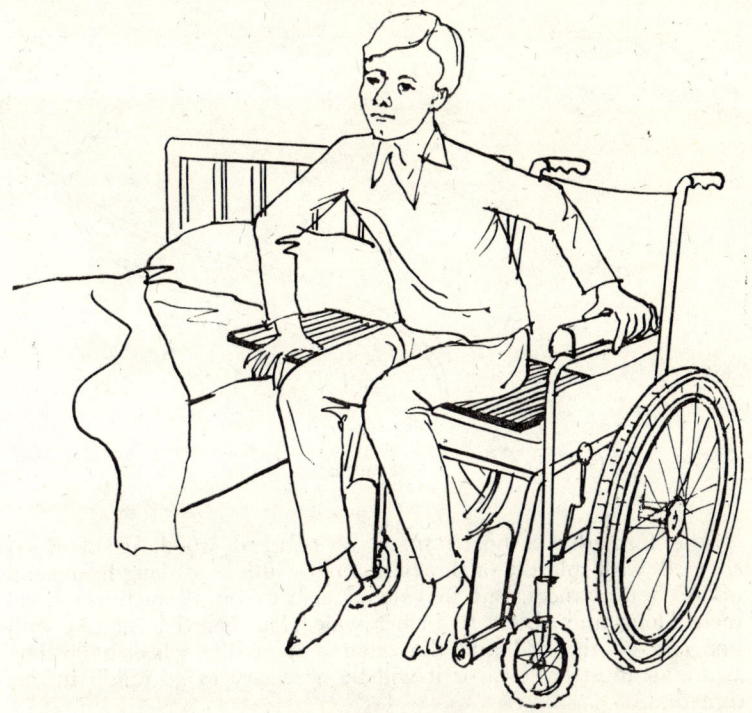

Sliding board to aid transfer from wheelchair to bed

bouncing and using the springing action to achieve a standing position.

The position of the bed in the room can also be a vital factor and it may be necessary to rearrange the room to give extra space. If the edge of the bed is placed against a wall it will remain stable for the person needing to push on it to rise, as well as giving more floor space for dressing and undressing.

In all cases, the mattress should be at least as wide as the frame of the bed, for a narrow mattress will cause damage to the skin by contact with the bedframe. If a hospital type bed is used, then a foam mattress with firm boards overlapping the frame is a useful precautionary measure.

Many people manage quite satisfactorily with the ordinary domestic bed, but the substitution of lightweight bedding, such as a continental quilt, and a firm mattress will be an added aid to mobility. Nylon sheets which are rather slippery will also make it easier to transfer on to a sliding board or direct to a wheelchair.

23

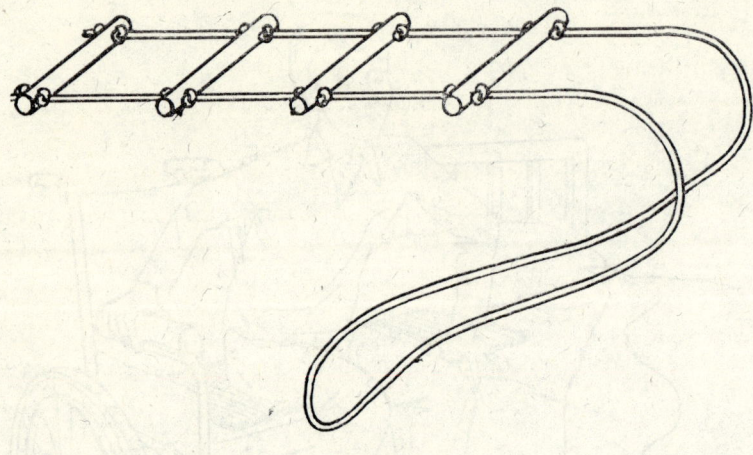

Bed ladder

The former is a board made of polished wood, or of wood covered with plastic or leather. The width and length depend upon circumstances, but in general is between 18 inches and 28 inches long and about 10 inches wide. The board is placed with one end on the bed and the other end on the wheelchair. The two ends must be level or it will be necessary to go uphill in one direction.

A rope ladder attached to the foot of the bed, or a self-lifting pole, will make it easier to rise to a sitting position in bed.

For the severely disabled person hoists, which are described below, can be provided to assist the transfer from bed to wheelchair or chair. Adjustable beds and ripple mattresses which can be used for nursing the severely disabled are described in the chapter on severe disability.

Lavatory

Going to the lavatory and getting on and off the lavatory seat, is often extremely difficult for disabled people.

The lavatory seat usually needs to be higher than is usual. Permanently raising the pedestal can be costly and is rarely necessary for there are many aids which can be used to overcome this problem.

First in importance is the position of grab rails alongside the pedestal, which provide extra support. Plastic and wooden clip-on seats are available commercially, but some people do not find them sufficiently comfortable or stable. A firm seat can be built over the pedestal at a convenient height and can be removed by

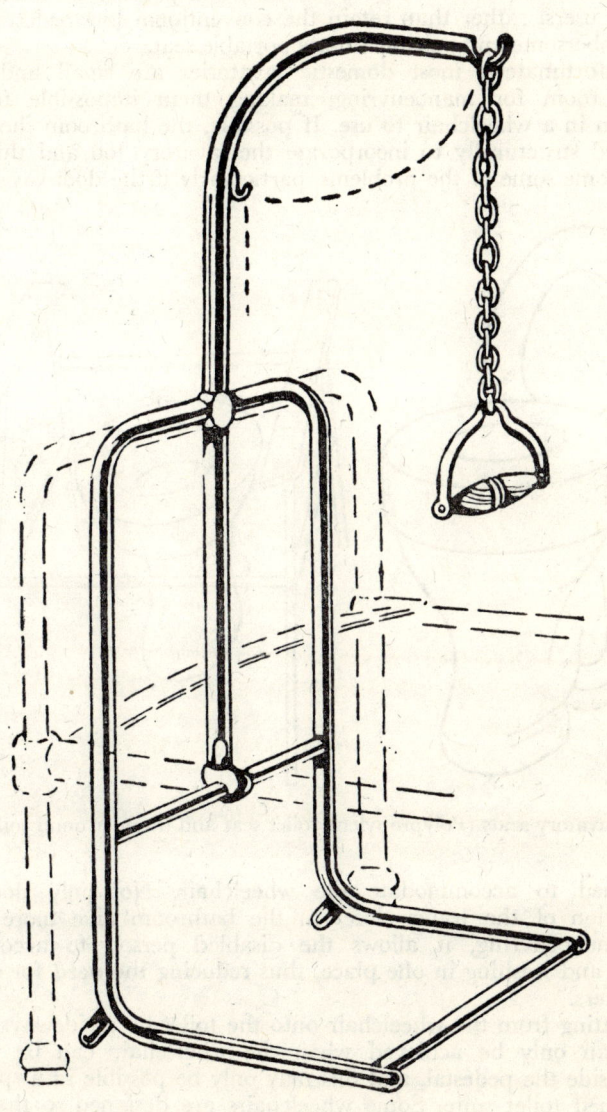

Lifting pole, free standing

other members of the family, but it is usually safer to install a permanent and stable high toilet seat, and provide a footstool for other users, rather than retain the conventional low pedestal with a cumbersome and possibly unsafe portable seat.

Unfortunately, most domestic lavatories are small and leave little room for manoeuvring, making them impossible for the person in a wheelchair to use. If possible, the bathroom should be altered structurally to incorporate the lavatory too and this may overcome some of the problems, particularly if the doorway can be

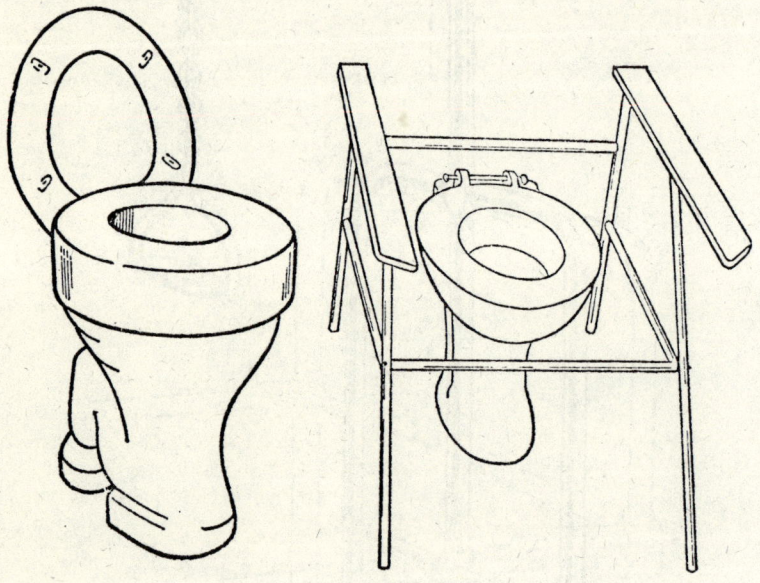

Lavatory seats (Polypropylene toilet seat and frame around toilet)

widened to accommodate the wheelchair. Not only does the inclusion of the water closet in the bathroom give more space for manoeuvring, it allows the disabled person to accomplish toilet and washing in one place, thus reducing the need for several transfers.

Getting from the wheelchair onto the toilet by a sideways transfer can only be achieved when the wheelchair can be placed alongside the pedestal, and this may only be possible in a specially designed toilet suite. Some wheelchairs are designed so that it is possible to transfer backwards on to the toilet, and other people transfer forwards and use the lavatory by sitting facing the "wrong" way.

For all these manoeuvres, the modern low flushing toilet suites are more awkward to negotiate than the old-fashioned type with a high cistern positioned well out of the way.

To be independent when using the lavatory is of paramount importance for the disabled person. Achieving this independence may mean the difference between being able to remain at home instead of living in a residential home or institution. It is an area of activity which may need the considerable experience and expertise of an occupational therapist before safe and efficient independence is achieved. It combines many activities, including dressing and undressing, washing and transferring, and the therapist or social worker experienced in this field will be able to advise on any necessary installations and alterations. There may be a simple solution, but if it is necessary for structural alterations to be made, or equipment to be supplied, local authority help may be available.

Bathing

Many baths are in small rooms with doorways which are difficult to negotiate and with fitments in awkward situations. The physical effort involved in getting in and out of the bath is considerable for an able bodied person, and large numbers of people with a disability encounter great difficulty in taking a bath. In many instances the situation can be made easier with aids and appliances, but in the final analysis it may be better to accept the need for someone else to be present to provide the necessary help.

Safety is the first consideration in the bathroom, and the provision of grab rails, alongside the bath and at each end, are an essential safety precaution to aid getting in and out of the bath. Anyone with weakness, tremor, paralysis or amputation is likely to slip, and the provision of a grab rail for support in any vulnerable situation such as lavatory, kitchen stairs or steps is essential, but above all the bathroom is the most dangerous situation, for the feet, hands and rails are wet and many people feel a bit faint as they rise to get out of the bath.

All grab rails in a bathroom should have a non-slip surface. If rails without a non-slip surface are put in the bathroom they should be covered with plastic tape material to give firm grip. Heated towel rails should be avoided if possible, because they could severely burn the person with diminished sensation who might use them for support.

Entry to the bath can be achieved by using a bath board made of a single polished or plastic covered board firmly fixed to the end of the bath, extended beyond the rim and supported by two legs.

A bath seat is a useful aid both for access and to enable the person to wash sitting rather than immersing in the bath. When one is used, great care should be taken to ensure that it is steady and will not slip. It is possible for a bath seat to be made to fit into a particular type of bath and designed so that it fits approximately midway between the bathboard and the bottom of the bath, the drop from one level to the next being the same. There are many bath seats available commercially, including some shaped

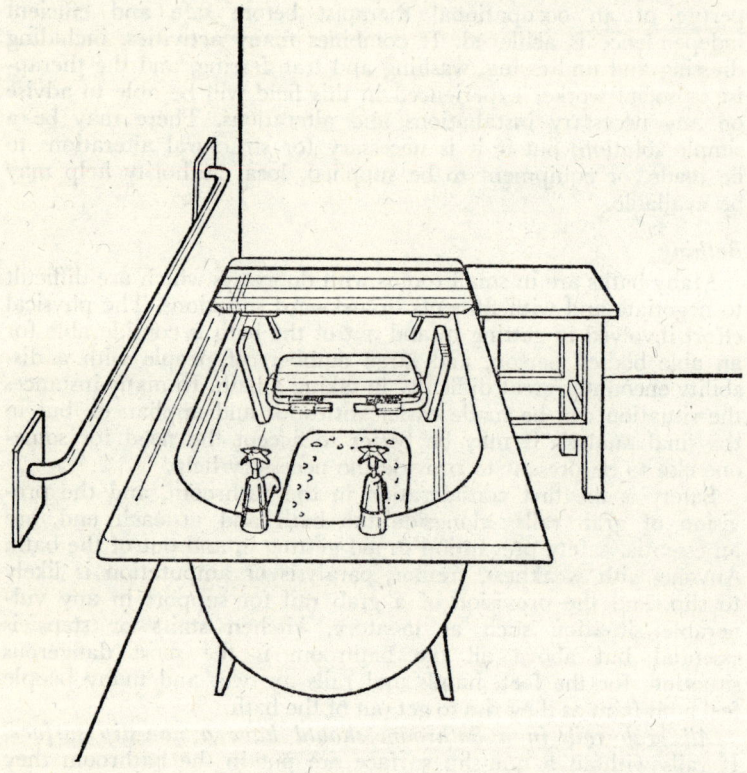

Bath aids: grab-rail, non-slip mat, two bath seats at different levels, and stool

like a toilet seat, which makes it easier to wash between the legs. But, whatever type is used, its stability in the bath is the essential factor. Further essential pieces of equipment are a non-slip rubber mat in the bottom of the bath and another beside the bath.

Many people find that the installation of a shower overcomes some of the difficulties involved in taking a bath. When installing a shower for a disabled person it is usually necessary to ensure that the "rose" is at shoulder height, otherwise the hair will get wet when only the body needs to be washed; and the shower should be sited where it is possbile to negotiate and transfer onto a suitable shower seat. These are costly installations and it is wise to seek advice from an occupational therapist or member of the social services who has experience in this type of installation, *before* consulting a plumber.

Another method of ensuring personal cleanliness is to put a bidet in the bathroom. This is particularly useful for those who experience difficulty in taking a bath.

Elderly people often decide to sleep downstairs when they find it difficult to go up and down stairs easily. If the bathroom is sited upstairs, this means that they no longer have access to it, therefore many of them do not bother to bath in the conventional way, and substitute an "all over wash" in the kitchen or living room. Unfortunately, this wash is usually attempted in very overcrowded conditions, for many old people are loath to part with their possessions and do not dispose of furniture to make room for their bed. They are, therefore, in a potentially dangerous situation for they often wash in front of the fire with a bowl placed on a table. If they are unsteady on their feet there is grave danger of an accident. Where possible, they should be gently encouraged to rearrange their accommodation to cope with this new way of living. If one or two pieces of furniture can be disposed of it will be easier for them to move around and for them to manage their toilet in more favourable conditions. A good steady chair, covered with a towel, and a bowl placed on a table at a height which can be reached easily and comfortably in a warm part of the room, but not near an open fire, are the most necessary items. It is better to carry the warm water in a jug to the bowl, rather than attempt to carry a bowl full of water. It is also better for the whole washing procedure to be done from the sitting position and a little at a time so that there is no fear of getting chilled.

Here again advice should be sought, because many local authorities have special arrangements for helping the disabled, the frail and the elderly to have a regular bath, either at home or in a special institution.

Seating

Again, it may seem irrelevant to the theme "Mobility" to discuss chairs, but it is as necessary to consider getting into and out of a chair as to consider its comfort while in use.

The selection of a suitable armchair is a very individual matter. Some people prefer a low slung, hammock type chair, others a chair with a good back support. The majority of elderly and disabled people require a chair with a high seat and firm back support, and of the right height for ease of getting up and down from it.

There are many chairs on the market which have been designed to overcome these problems. The seat heights vary from sixteen to twenty-four inches from the ground, and the arms are sturdily made to withstand the extra pressure needed when using them for support to reach the standing position. Some chairs have a self-lifting cushion to raise one to the standing position by the use of specially arranged springs, and there are lifting seats which are portable and can be used in any chair. Advice on seating problems can be given by the social services, or the Furniture Traders Association can be approached for stockists' addresses.

Many elderly people become very attached to a favourite arm-chair, and tend to sit surrounded by cushions for extra padding, which are useless when they need to rise. If they can be encouraged

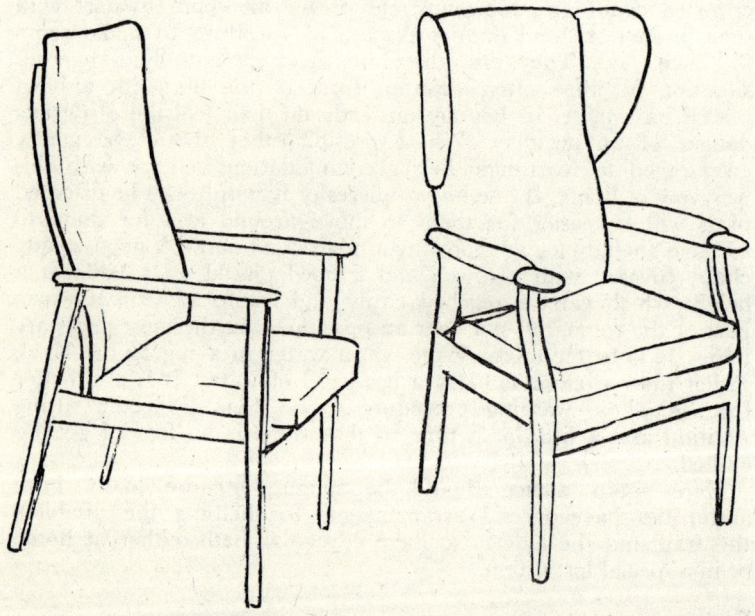

Chairs: the high seat, lumbar curve of the back, support for the head and solid arms make this type very suitable for many elderly and disabled people

to dispense with some of the smaller cushions and add a firm rubber cushion about four inches deep to the seat, they will often find it is much easier to get in and out of the chair.

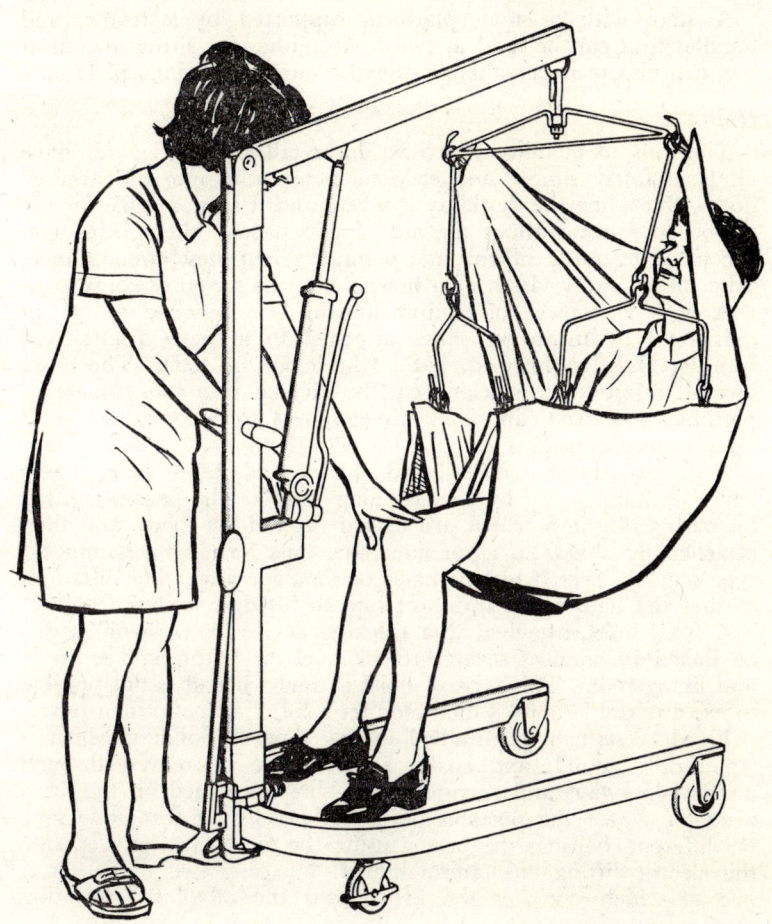

Hoist sling with divided legs and toilet aperture

Kneeling

Kneeling is particularly difficult for anyone with stiff knees and hips, and it is often wiser to find other ways of doing tasks for which kneeling is necessary. A long handled reacher or pick-up stick is very useful for picking things up from the floor, or for reaching difficult corners with a duster. Long handled dustpans and brushes can be used for sweeping up crumbs and dust and squeeze mops and impregnated polishing mops will cope with floor cleaning problems. (See Home-making and Housework, p. 64.)

31

A stool with a small platform supported by a frame, and handles that can be used at two levels, either for sitting or kneeling, can also prove invaluable. (See Leisure : gardening, p. 117.)

Hoists

The aids to mobility which we have talked about so far have all been fairly simple and easy to incorporate into the average home. But when the disability is severe and it is impossible for the person to move without the aid of two people, then lifting can become dangerous, difficult and painful. When these circumstances arise, then the provision of a hoist should be seriously considered.

A hoist is a piece of equipment which is designed to lift an individual by means of slings attached to a metal frame, and transport him to his bed, bath, wheelchair or toilet. There are several different types which can be divided into two categories, portable and fixed, and they are designed to carry a weight of up to twenty stones.

A portable hoist is constructed of steel and stands on a chassis which is manoeuvred by easy running castors. The person is lifted by means of slings which are placed around the body and then attached by chains to a spreader bar, thus forming a hammock-type seat. A lever, which is hand or foot operated, then lifts him so that the helper can transport him to his destination.

A fixed hoist, attached to a tracking device on the ceiling, can be linked to connect several rooms, such as bathroom, bedroom and living room. This type of hoist is used when it is not possible to use a portable hoist, which requires a lot of space to manoeuvre.

Fixed hoists can be installed in any type of building which is structurally sound, and enable a person to be moved through narrow doorways and corridors. The slings are used on the same principle as for the portable hoist, but the lifting technique may be different, because the person using the fixed hoist can operate the electric lifting mechanism himself by using two nylon cords, one of which operates the lifting and the other the lowering mechanism.

Because the installation of a fixed hoist entails a certain amount of structural alteration, it may be most suitable for the individual who can adapt his surroundings to his specific needs, rather than for the person who is living in a house used by a number of other people.

A hoist attached to a gantry is also available. Although this is a portable hoist, in that it can be moved if the person moves house, it is principally designed to stay in one position, over the bed, with the wheelchair and commode placed at either side of the bed for easy transfer. The controls are operated in the same way as the fixed hoist and can be self-operated.

The slings which support the body in the hoist are made of

• •

thick canvas, nylon or terylene, and are made in a variety of shapes and sizes to meet individual requirements. It is important to know the different types which are available, for it may be necessary to try several designs before a comfortable one is found. There are also slings which stay in position whilst the person is in the bath, thus making the transfer in and out easier.

Hoists are available commercially, but are relatively expensive. The majority of people who need hoists will have them supplied

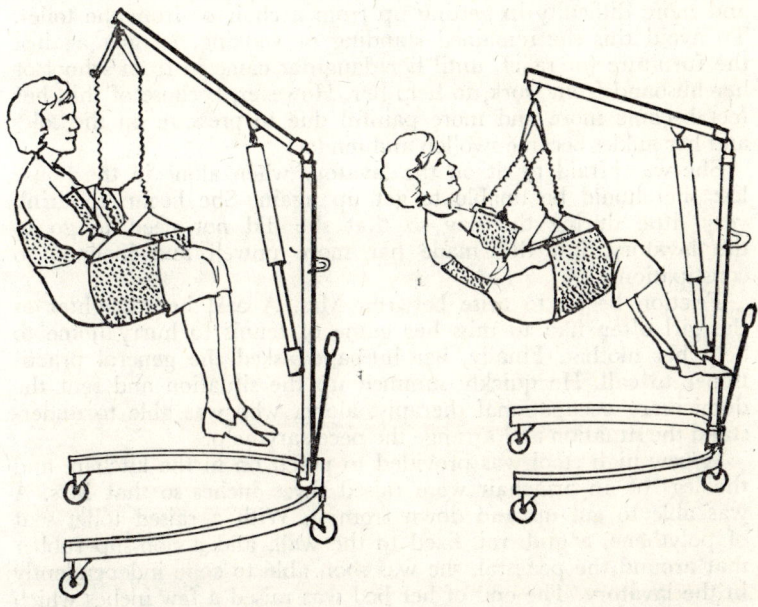

Use of slings with portable hoist:
Upright position

Use of slings with portable hoist:
Lying position

through the local authority. Often the patient will be assessed at a hospital rehabilitation department, because it is wise to try out the various types of hoists before installing one at home. Most local authorities have a small supply of standard portable hoists, but often they do not have a wide range of slings, or the facility to assess a person on a fixed hoist. However, the domiciliary occupational therapist and the hospital occupational therapy department will usually collaborate in achieving a practical test and training session before installing the hoist in their patient's home.

CASE HISTORY

Mrs. A had had rheumatoid arthritis for many years, but had managed to look after her home, husband and daughter very well. They had moved into a bungalow so that she had no stairs to climb, and it was not until her daughter reached adolescence that real difficulty arose.

Mrs. A was not unduly worried by pain which was well controlled by aspirin her main concern was increasing stiffness in her joints, especially her hips and knees. Consequently, she had more and more difficulty in getting up from a chair or from the toilet. To avoid this she remained standing or walking, leaning against the furniture for relief, until her daughter came in from school or her husband from work, to help her. However, because of this, her feet became more and more painful due to pressure on the soles and her ankles became swollen and tender.

She was afraid to sit on the lavatory when alone in the house lest she should be unable to get up again. She began to drink very little during the day so that she did not need to go to the lavatory, but this made her more unwell and inclined to constipation.

Friction began to arise between Mrs. A and her daughter as the girl often had to miss her game of tennis to hurry home to help her mother. Finally, her husband asked the general practitioner to call. He quickly summed up the situation and sent the domiciliary occupational therapist along, who was able to understand the situation and arrange the necessary help.

A new high stool was provided to perch on in the kitchen, and the legs of an armchair were raised three inches so that Mrs. A was able to get up and down from it. With a raised toilet seat of polythene, a grab rail fixed to the wall, and a non-slip rubber mat around the pedestal, she was soon able to cope independently in the lavatory. The end of her bed was raised a few inches which helped to reduce the swelling in her ankles, and her general health soon improved.

3

Wheelchairs

IN the first century B.C. Asclepiades wrote :

> Of all the exercises which have been devised for the treatment
> of diseases, assuredly the easiest and by far the most convenient
> is transportation, which the patient can use even if he is so
> infirm he cannot move himself. He can be busy in the fields,
> outdoors, enjoy the sunshine, be restored by fresh air; he can
> be moved in a quiet and pleasant way as long as he pleases.

This is still true today for many thousands of wheelchair users,
who are able to enjoy a greater personal freedom and a happier
life than would be possible if they had no means of transportation.

Wheelchairs are now provided under the National Health
Service in this country. Applications are made through a general
practitioner, who may be able to prescribe one himself, or else he
may send the request through to the local centre where clinics
are held, and where people can try a variety of wheelchairs for
size, comfort and suitability.

There are many different types of wheelchair, both self-
propelled and attendant propelled, and they can be classified as
follows : folding or rigid; self-propelled chairs or attendant propelled chairs; indoor or outdoor chairs; standard weight or lightweight chairs; outsize, adults, junior or child-size.

Attendant propelled wheelchairs have small wheels, which do
not need to be within reach of the person in the chair. They may
be small for easy transport in a car, or large if they are only to
be used for pushing the occupant out for shopping or pleasure.
The latter are like large, well-sprung pushchairs, and have a
chassis similar to a child's pram. Comfort is the dictating factor in
their design, and they can be obtained in child, junior, adult and
outsizes.

The smaller wheelchair, which is also attendant propelled, is
intended mainly for transport purposes for which it can be easily
folded. It is not suitable for pushing for long distances or over
rough or soft ground.

Self-propelled wheelchairs, with front wheels used for propelling, are the easiest type to use indoors when manoeuvring

on carpets. On the other hand, they impede sideways transfer and close forward approach, they cannot negotiate kerbs, and may tip forward if pushed by an attendant.

Rear-wheeled, self-propelled wheelchairs are most suitable for outdoor and general use. Most rear-wheeled self-propelling chairs have tilting levers for an attendant to use when negotiating kerbs. These are the most commonly prescribed chairs, and there are

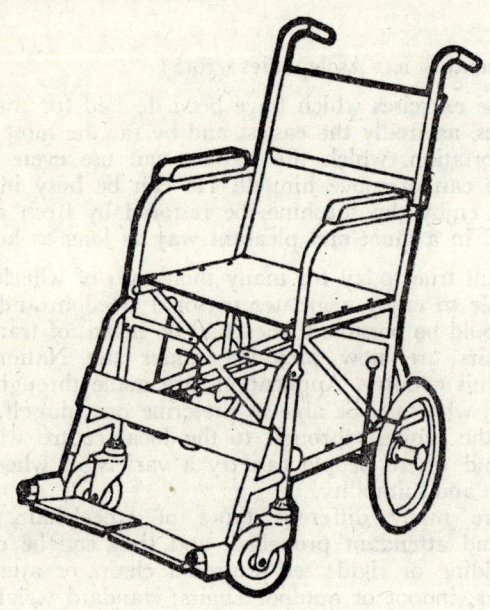

Car transit wheelchair

more than twenty types to choose from together with many variations on the standard attendant or self-propelled chairs.

The sides and armrests can be fixed or detachable, depending on the individual's need or preference. Some people need fixed sides to give them a firm grip for manoeuvring in and out of the chair, or for lifting the chair into their car. Others must have detachable sides to allow for sideways transfer. Detachable sides also reduce the weight and size of the chair for folding into the car boot, as they can be removed and lifted in separately.

The height of the armrests can be adjusted depending on the type of cushioning used and individual comfort. Some of the proprietary brands of wheelchairs have detachable sides which are supplied in different heights. Others can have a shaped front which will allow the wheelchair to approach closer to a table or a desk, for which special armrests can be supplied. In addition, reversible sides are available. These can be used both for close approach to tables and reversed, when necessary, to a normal height to push on when transferring.

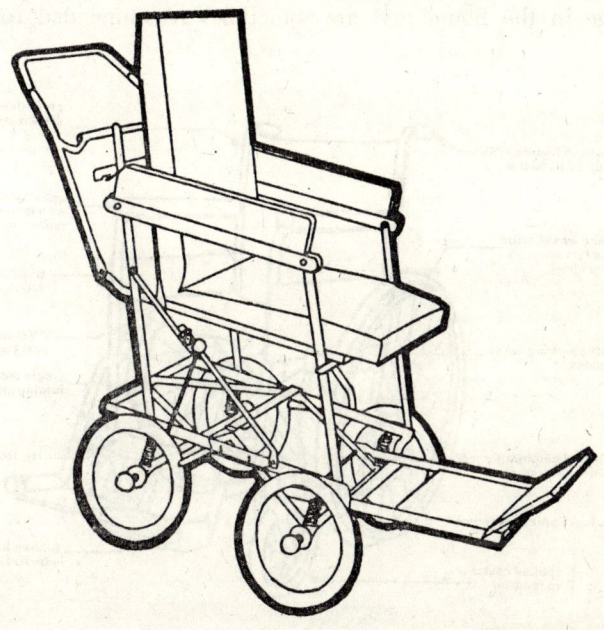

Attendant propelled wheelchair

Most Department of Health wheelchairs have twenty-two inch pneumatic rear wheels, but wheel sizes can be varied according to the space available at home and the patient's special needs. The larger the wheels, the greater the leverage, and the easier it will be to propel the chair, but large wheels present difficulties for those who are likely to transfer sideways out of their wheelchair. However, rear wheels of twenty inch diameter can be supplied. As these are usually below the level of the seat to transfer sideways is not difficult. Large front wheels of any size are best used by people who are able to transfer forwards or who can stand and turn and sit again. Handrims and capstans can be fitted to aid grip. These are usually made of metal but they can be varied and the capstan knobs designed so that they can be pushed by the palm of the hand or the knuckles.

Pneumatic tyres are better for outdoor use as they have some element of springing and give a better grip on wet surfaces. But they do puncture, and a severely disabled person could be rendered helpless should this happen. They may also be difficult for someone with weak arms to manoeuvre, particularly on carpets, because of the higher degree of friction. Solid tyres are easier to manage in the house and are sometimes recommended for self-

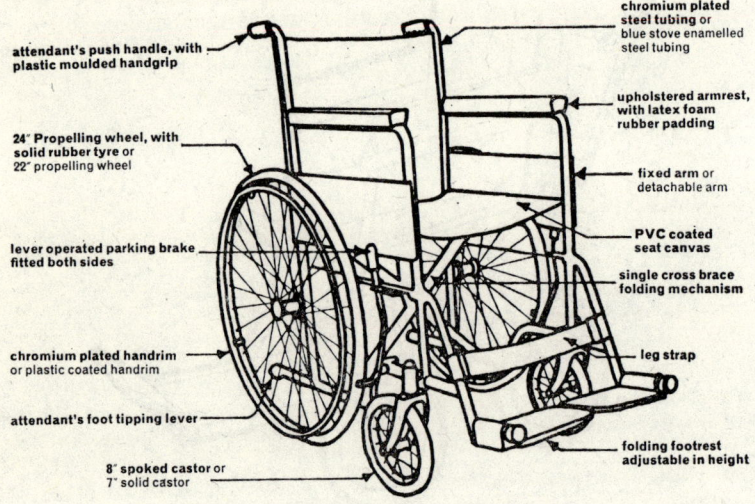

chromium plated
steel tubing or
blue stove enamelled
steel tubing

attendant's push handle, with
plastic moulded handgrip

upholstered armrest,
with latex foam
rubber padding

24″ Propelling wheel, with
solid rubber tyre or
22″ propelling wheel

fixed arm or
detachable arm

lever operated parking brake
fitted both sides

PVC coated
seat canvas

single cross brace
folding mechanism

chromium plated handrim
or plastic coated handrim

leg strap

attendant's foot tipping lever

8″ spoked castor or
7″ solid castor

folding footrest
adjustable in height

Self propelled wheelchair for which many variations are possible

propelling wheelchairs, but the tread wears, and the brakes may fail to grip well. In general, pneumatic tyres are to be recommended.

Most wheelchair brakes depend on mechanical linkage which enables a metal lever to bite into the tyres of two of the wheels. This gradually wears away solid tyres, making the brakes less effective. Pneumatic tyres exert better grip provided they are well pumped up. But, whichever type of tyres is used, careful attention to brake maintenance is essential for continued safety, because many people use their chairs for support when standing or transferring, or use the arms for support when dropping into the chair, and faulty brakes could cause the chair to move backwards, or to tip.

Some people manage to manoeuvre a wheelchair on flat surfaces but cannot manage to push it up a slope because of its tendency to run backwards between forward pushes. There are two types of uni-directional brakes available, one fitting onto the undercarriage of the chair, the other fitting the wheel. In each case, there is no impediment to forward movement, but the brake prevents the chair running backwards.

For the one-handed wheelchair user, chairs are available with the propelling handrims for both wheels on the same side of the chair. Many young people become very adept at using these on level ground, but can rarely manage slopes. Elderly people are not so successful at managing single arm propelling chairs. An easier technique is to propel with one hand and one foot, with the hand propelling forward and the foot correcting the tendency to turn. Again this is suitable on level ground, particularly indoors and many people with strokes find it a most successful technique.

As with an armchair, the required angle of the backrest of the wheelchair will vary from person to person. Some people like sitting upright and others prefer to recline. Care should be taken that the angle of the reclining back is not so great that it causes the user to slide forward in the chair, for this makes it difficult to propel and to sit comfortably while eating or working. Most wheelchairs can be fitted with a headrest extension, but as this follows the line of the back of the chair it is often not in the best position to support the head. Simple neckrests can be made to attach to such an extension, but they are best specially built.

Cushions can make or mar most people's comfort when sitting in a chair, and the person in a wheelchair can be made very uncomfortable by using soft cushions, air rings and similar emblems of comfort. Air rings predispose to pressure sores, and deep soft cushions successfully immobilize anyone with severe disability. Soft upholstery, covered with leathercloth on a firm plywood base is the most suitable form of cushioning for it will support the person and allow easy transfer from the chair. When it is used in a folding wheelchair it can easily be removed, thus minimizing the space needed for storage either in the car or in the hallway. Sheepskin covers for seat cushions can also be supplied through the health service, or an alternating pressure cushion will relieve pressure and discomfort and prevent pressure sores. There are many new materials for filling cushions now available.

Water cushions are also available, but these devices are really designed to prevent the development of pressure sores in those people who are prone to do so—those with diminished sensation, considerable muscle wasting, or circulatory deficiency. As with the chair, the cushions must be individually prescribed and most of the special cushions and special chairs can only be prescribed by a hospital consultant.

Wheelchairs for children

There is a growing need to provide suitable wheelchairs for severely disabled children so that they are able to obtain mobility at an age when they would normally crawl. The small, self-propelling chariot is useful for a very small child, particularly the severe spina bifida. A lightweight folding pushchair known as the Baby Buggy and a larger model, the Major Buggy, which can

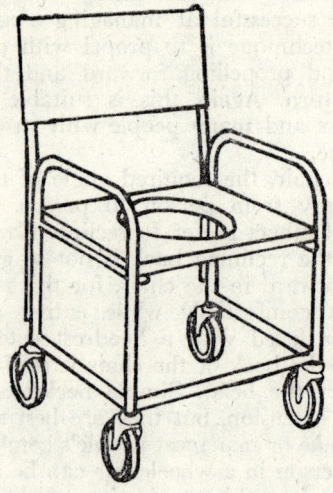

Mobile commode or toilet chair

be folded and carried with one hand, is particularly suitable for taking on public transport or in a car, and can be prescribed under the National Health Service.

When travelling in a car, a proprietary child's car seat, if firmly attached to the seat of the car, is as suitable as anything.

As the child grows, he can be issued with a standard child-size wheelchair which can be self-propelled or attendant propelled. There are special models suitable only for indoor use, which are particularly designed for some spastic and spina-bifida children.

A three-wheeled tricycle, similar to the type used by many children, can be issued to a child with muscular weakness who does not need to rely entirely on a wheelchair.

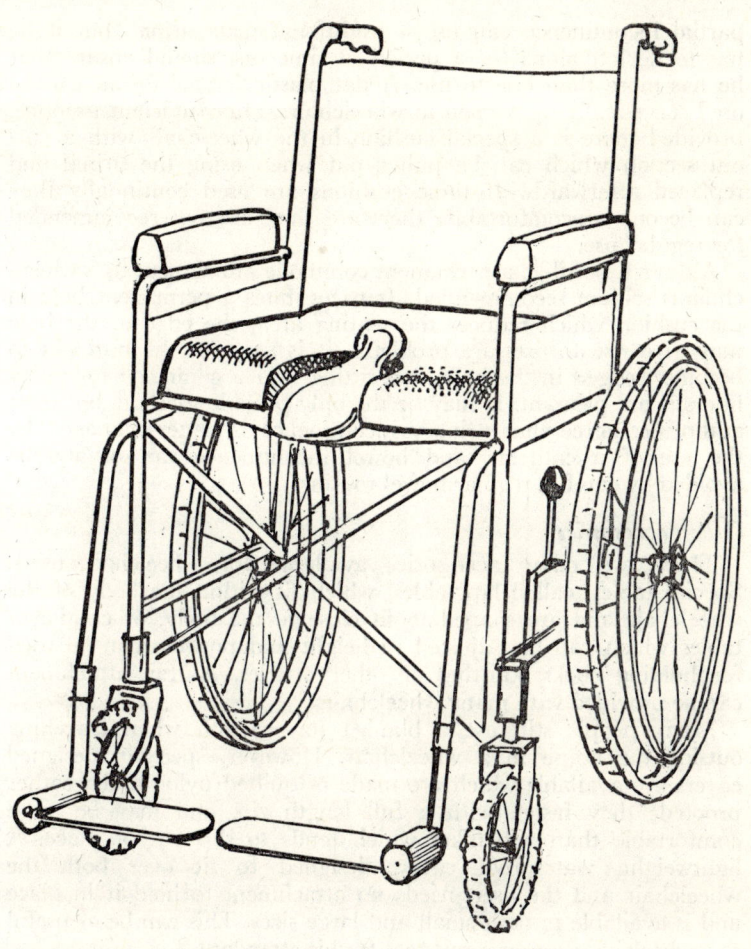

Hard based cushion with cut-out to accommodate urinal

Toilet adaptations to wheelchairs

Wheelchair users who are incontinent present special problems, and it is usually advisable to seek medical advice when in difficulty.

Although commode chairs and sani-chairs, designed to be wheeled over the toilet, are available, they can only be used by transferring from wheelchair on to the commode chair, and this presents its own problems. Cushions which incorporate urinals or bedpans are also subject to accident or failure. The man with

41

partial incontinence can use a traditional male urinal, but if he has to be left alone for a period of time one should ensure that he has more than one to use. A flat plastic female urinal can be used successfully by women in wheelchairs, after sufficient practice, provided there is a special cushion in the wheelchair with a cut-out section which can be pulled out when using the urinal and replaced afterwards. If these cushions are used continually they can become uncomfortable, therefore they are not recommended for regular use.

Although possible, a permanent commode attachment to a wheelchair is seldom recommended. It necessitates a permanent hole in the cushion which reduces the seating area, the edge of the hole may give rise to pressure problems, it is easy for the buttocks to become wedged in the hole, and sitting over a commode for many hours is not pleasant. It may be the only possible solution, but most authorities agree that urinary incontinence is better managed by the use of a catheter, and bowel incontinence can usually be avoided by careful, regular bowel routine.

Other accessories

There are many accessories available for wheelchair users. Special tables, called lap tables, which fit within the body of the wheelchair and are shaped to fit close to the body, or cantilever tables which can be adjusted in height and position can be used for holding books, knitting or other articles. A tray attachment can be provided with many wheelchairs.

Many people still use a blanket for warmth when travelling outside the house in a wheelchair. However, specially designed covers are available which are made of quilted nylon and weather proofed; they fasten with a full length zip, and may be more comfortable than a blanket which tends to slip out of place. A lightweight, waterproof cover, designed to fit over both the wheelchair and the user, needs no attachment to hold it in place and is available in both small and large sizes. This can be as useful to a wheelchair user as a raincoat for his attendant.

Another problem for the self-propelling wheelchair user is the dirt and wear on the sleeves of clothing. Simple sleevelets made of plastic or thick nylon material and gathered at the wrist-band will help to prevent this.

Sore hands can be prevented by using a hand-protector made of an oval piece of pimpled rubber stitched to a soft leather base and attached to the wrists by straps fastened with Velcro.

CASE HISTORY

Peter was a bright little boy with spina bifida. Partially paralysed from the waist down he managed to walk slowly and with a struggle, wearing calipers and using elbow crutches.

At the small junior school in the village Peter worked very hard, and his parents were proud when he passed his eleven-plus examination and gained a place in the secondary school. Peter was very excited and eager to go to the "big" school. Unfortunately it was indeed a very big school, the distances he had to walk were considerable, he could not manage to keep up with the other boys and was always last in getting to the classrooms. He soon got very tired and dispirited, his school work deteriorated and he became pale, apathetic and unhappy.

At the hospital where he attended for a regular check-up, the doctor noticed this change in his condition, quickly found out the problem and suggested that Peter should use a wheelchair at school for greater speed, safety, and to spare his limited energy.

Unfortunately, Peter's father was appalled at this suggestion, which he thought an admission of defeat, and feared that by using a wheelchair his son would become a permanent invalid. So Peter, very unwillingly, returned to school without a wheelchair, and quickly became more and more exhausted.

A few weeks later the doctor asked the medical social worker to call on the family to see how things were going on. She also called at the school and arranged a meeting with the headmaster, Peter and his parents. The headmaster pointed out that there was no problem in Peter using a wheelchair at school and he thought it would be a very sensible solution. Peter's disability made it unlikely that he would be able to seek employment requiring physical ability, therefore he needed the best academic education available, including all the social amenities that a good school can offer. After much discussion, Peter's father realised that by using a wheelchair his son would have greater mobility, be happier and much less tired.

At the start of his second term in the schoool Peter arrived in his smart new wheelchair, with a clip attached to the side to carry his elbow crutches for walking short distances. Many of the boys were interested in this new piece of equipment, but after an initial focus of attention on the chair, it was soon taken for granted. It took Peter some weeks to regain his self-confidence, but as he no longer became so tired and was able to keep up with the other boys, he began to really enjoy his school life.

4

Personal Appearance

MOST people like to present a pleasing appearance, and physical disability is no excuse for not doing so. With a little effort and a few aids it is possible for most people to continue to take a pride in their personal appearance, which, in turn, will make it easier to establish and maintain social contacts.

When planning a daily routine of washing and dressing, the first necessity is hot water for washing. Unless the washbasin is easily accessible and of the correct height and it is possible to stand without support, it is better for a bowl of hot water to be placed on a table in a more accessible room.

As the first consideration is for the patient's safety, the table should be so positioned that it is possible to cope with most of the washing while seated either in a wheelchair or on a chair covered with a towel. It may be unrealistic for some people to attempt to wash all over every day, and if disability is severe it may be more sensible to accept help and prevent undue tiredness. A planned programme of washing so that different parts of the body are washed on certain days, in a room that is warm and comfortable, is the least that one should aim for.

One of the most useful aids for washing is a plastic foam mop, such as those used for washing dishes, for the long handle makes it possible to reach the face and other parts of the body without too much effort. A long handled bath sponge is also very effective for this purpose. Nailbrushes with a curved handgrip are easier to use than the type that need to be gripped.

When taking a bath a long handled sponge, and a small hand shower attached to the taps, will make the washing process easier. When using the shower attachment the flow of water should be carefully balanced.

The person with arthritis may find it difficult to grip a flannel or the soap. But this can be overcome by using a small piece of soap inserted in terry towelling mittens, or soap holders.

The use of talcum powder, in moderation, and deodorants will help to preserve freshness for longer periods. when it is too difficult to wash more than once a day.

A warm room, and a method of warming the towels are probably the most useful requirements for drying oneself. When it is difficult to grip and control a towel sufficiently to reach and apply pressure to the body, a large warm bath towel or towelling cloak which is large enough to cover most of the body will act as an effective drying agent if the body is wriggled underneath it. A length of roller towel, with the ends turned back to form mittens, is useful for drying the back and the legs. Or, if the grip is weak a pair of thick towelling mittens can be used to pat the body dry. The one-handed person can attach the towel to a wall hook which will hold one end while he manoeuvres the other end to dry himself.

Weak grip often makes it difficult to brush the teeth. To overcome this, rest the elbows on the edge of the basin, or table holding the bowl, with the free hand grip the wrist of the hand holding the brush and move the head to manoeuvre the brush round the teeth, thus avoiding wrist movement. Sometimes it helps to lengthen or alter the shape of the handle of the toothbrush to a more suitable angle. Many people who are unable to manage other ways find an electric toothbrush invaluable.

Removing dentures can be hazardous for those with severe arthritis of the upper limbs, and it is possible to have a long handled denture holder made in an occupational therapy department, to assist in putting in and taking out the dentures.

The current fashion for beards may provide a satisfactory and practical solution to the shaving problem for some disabled men, but for those who wish to continue shaving an electric razor is often the best solution. If it is not possible to hold it in the usual way, it can be attached to a bracket at a suitable height. Otherwise, a special hand attachment can be made in an occupational therapy department, which will make it possible to place the razor in a leather hand-held pocket so that it is not necessary to grip it.

Light make-up is now the fashion for women, and much advice is given in magazines on the correct ways to achieve the best effect. The disabled woman or teenage girl can make the most of her appearance by studying the art of make-up. It may be necessary to use long handled attachments to hold such items as lipstick and pads for applying creams and powder, but these aids can be provided through occupational therapy departments. A mirror placed at a convenient height and in a good light is very important. If it is not possible to get close enough to a pedestal or hanging mirror, a special mirror has been designed which hangs around the neck and can be adjusted to the necessary angle.

Clean, healthy looking hair is very important, and for the person in a wheelchair it will probably be the first thing that is noticed about their appearance. Long or short hair always looks better if it is clean and shining, therefore regular washing and

45

appropriate shampoos for hair conditioning and to prevent dandruff are necessary. It is usually better if hair-washing is done by another member of the family or a friend, for it is very difficult to achieve single-handed. The use of a small hand-shower attached to the bath or basin taps often makes the procedure easier. If the shower is attached to the bath taps it may be possible to wash the hair at the same time as bathing, but great care should be taken in controlling the temperature and flow of the water.

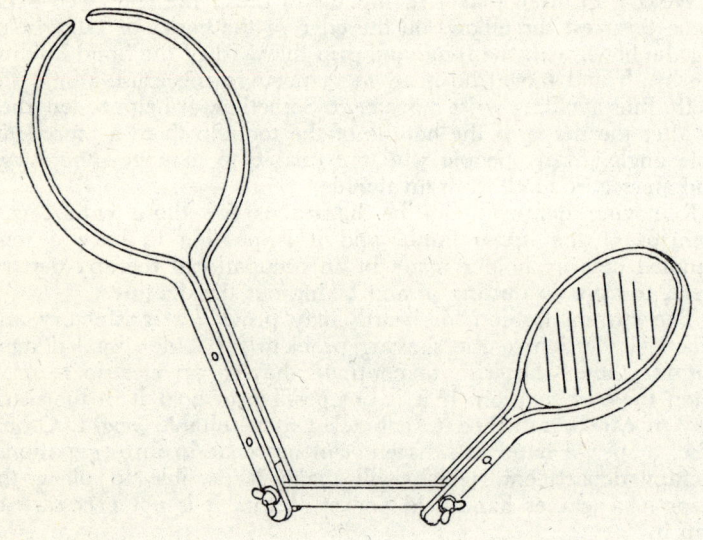

Make-up mirror which can be hung around the neck

Long hair is currently fashionable for all young people, and if well washed and groomed it can look attractive, but is undoubtedly more difficult to maintain than short hair. Regular visits to a good hair-stylist (bearing in mind that, on average, hair grows a quarter of an inch in a month) should not make it too difficult to keep a short and fashionable hairstyle. Some hairdressing salons or technical colleges run practice sessions for apprentices which make it possible to have quite a cheap hairdo once in a while.

Manicuring nails can be very difficult for anyone with weak hands and arms for it requires a variety of movements and quite strong grip. Emery boards, which can be bought in packs from most chemists shops, are used by many disabled people for they

46

are light and flexible to use, but it may still prove too tiring to manicure the nails of both hands at one session. There is an electrically operated nail file on the market, but it is part of a complete make-up kit, and is not available as a separate item.

Toe nails may be too difficult for elderly and arthritic people to manicure. The chiropodist employed by the local authority may be able to give this service if a member of the family cannot help. Care of the toenails is very important, for if they remain uncut they will become ingrown and require surgical treatment. Elderly people with circulation problems, and those with diabetes, should take considerable care to ensure that their feet and nails receive proper attention.

5

Dressing and Clothing

PHYSICAL disability often draws attention to itself by the person's appearance. A deformity or unnatural movement may be conspicuous, but even if it is not, the person concerned often feels that it is so. Thus disguising or compensating for a deformity may be of considerable concern to some people. Much can be done by the careful selection or adaptation of standard clothing, for there is no reason why people with a physical disability should not wear attractive clothes although their individual requirements may need special consideration.

Dressing

The process of dressing requires balance, co-ordination, reach, strength and dexterity, all of which are taken for granted in normal circumstances. But when difficulty presents itself, then it is necessary to find new techniques for the same procedures.

Undressing, for instance, is more than taking one's clothes off, it is also a preparation for dressing. If the whole process is done in one part of the room, preferably near the clothes cupboard so that the clothes can be hung up as they are taken off, and the clothes for the next day arranged near at hand, it will be both labour and time saving. Clothes should not be allowed to fall to the floor inside out, as this will only present greater problems when dressing again. As the clothes are taken off they should be folded ready for use the next day, or placed in a laundry basket. The order in which they are taken off is likely to be in reverse to the order in which they will be put on again; but the sequence of these manoeuvres will, of course, depend upon the individual. If help is needed, such as support when putting on the garments for the lower part of the body (underpants, trousers, socks, shoes or calipers), it is best to decide when this help is needed so that it can be timed to fit in with the family routine.

Dressing aids, such as dressing sticks which are designed to pull on clothing such as skirts, trousers, straps of upper garments, sweaters and blouses, or stocking aids or sock aids, long handled shoe horns and pick up sticks, will all prove helpful, and can be provided through the domiciliary occupational therapy departments.

Many people experience difficulty in balancing when putting on socks, stockings or shoes. Sitting on a dining chair or a bed so that the arms are not restricted and crossing one leg over the other to avoid bending is generally the safest way to overcome this problem.

General advice

When dressing is difficult it is better to choose uncomplicated clothing, and to aim for garments fewer in number but thicker in quality, thus a warm slip will dispense with the need to wear a vest, and lined dresses and skirts may do away with the need to wear a slip. If there is some restriction or weakness of grip loose styles will be easier for dressing, and, with a few minor alterations, many "off the peg" clothes can be made easier to get on and off.

An invaluable aid when adapting clothes is elastic, for it can be used wherever extra stretch is needed. Shoulder straps, waistbands, ties and cuff fastenings can all be altered with elastic to make dressing easier, and elastic shoe laces can be obtained commercially if lace-up shoes are worn.

As far as possible, all tight fitting items, such as belts, should be avoided. They are very uncomfortable for someone sitting in a wheelchair, and a man using crutches will find that elastic braces which keep the trousers well positioned and expand with shoulder movement, will be better than a belt for keeping his trousers in place.

The wheelchair user is strongly advised to choose garments which are generous in size. Slacks and trousers which are oversize in crutch and seat will be more comfortable. A large size usually means a longer leg length, but it is quite easy to shorten these.

Shopping for clothes

Shopping for clothes may be difficult, and trying them on both frustrating and tiring. Some of the large department stores carry a wide range of clothes and also have lifts which make it easier to move around the different departments. Large changing rooms are also more likely to be found in these stores, and the extra services of goods on approval and exchange if unsuitable are usually good. Reputable mail order firms also carry a wide range of clothing, much of it from well known manufacturers. The advantage of ordering through this system is, of course, that the goods are sent direct to the home where they can be tried on in privacy, and returned if they are unsuitable.

Adaptations to standard clothing

Simple adaptations to clothing will often make it easier to dress. Frequently the openings of garments are not large enough to give sufficient access for limbs with restricted movement. Existing zips

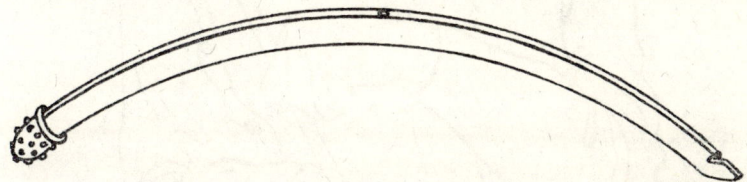

Dressing stick made from a coat-hanger. A stationer's thimble on one end of the curved stick will cling to the clothes. A notch cut in the other end will help in pulling up shoulder straps

or buttons can easily be removed, and the seams unstitched to provide extra length. Then a longer zip or buttons can be stitched into the extended opening. An extra opening at the waistband of skirts or dresses makes it easier to slip them on and off.

If jacket sleeves are tight or difficult to negotiate over stiff shoulders and arms, the inside seams of the sleeves can be un-stitched and replaced with a long zip fastener, or a gusset stitched underarm may provide more freedom of movement. The inside seam of the trouser legs can also be replaced with a long zip, thus doing away with the difficulty of pulling the trousers on over calipers or deformed limbs. A gusset sewn in the crutch of slacks or trousers will be more comfortable for the person sitting in a wheelchair. It may make the waist larger, but this extra material can be taken up by inserting elastic in the waistband.

49

Using a dressing stick

Handicapped people often get into a tangle as they dress and undress. Again, some simple adaptations are helpful. For example, when putting on a coat or cardigan over a blouse or shirt there is a tendency for the inner sleeve to be pushed up inside the coat.

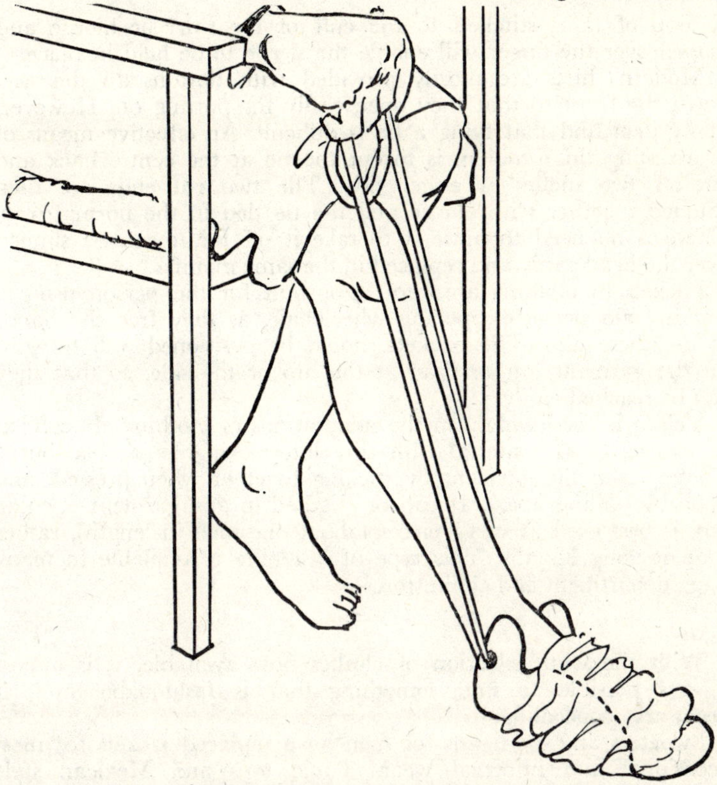

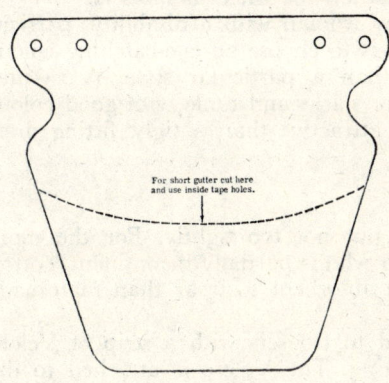

A stocking gutter made of plastic will help the person who cannot reach his or her feet to pull on socks or stockings. Two cotton tapes, 48 ins. long, are fixed in the holes

For short gutter cut here and use inside tape holes.

Pattern for plastic stocking aid

The stocking is gathered up down to its foot and it is then slipped over the gutter with the gathered part held in the indentation. The toes must be pushed well into the stocking before pulling on the tapes. If the ankles are stiff a shorter gutter should be used

A loop of tape, stitched to the cuff of the shirt or blouse and looped over the finger will enable the sleeve to be held in place.

Modern shirts are mostly provided with buttons all the way down the front so that they open easily for putting on. However, many men find that tying a tie is difficult. An effective means of overcoming this problem is to cut the tie at the centre back and cut off two inches at either side. The two cut ends are then stitched together with elastic and the tie tied in the normal way. There is no need to untie it to take it off for it can be slipped over the head easily and replaced in the same manner.

Pockets in clothing are very important for the person using a walking aid or self-propelling wheelchair, as they free the hands to use these aids. The pockets should be positioned well forward on the garment, rather than at the hip or the side, so that they can be reached easily.

Velcro is used widely in the adaptations of clothing. It consists of two strips of material with tiny interlocking loops, like burrs. These fasten the garment by sticking together when pressed, and open by pulling apart. It can be stitched to any garment opening and is best used in small pieces (about one inch in length), rather than in long lengths. This type of fastening is available in many large department and chain stores.

Styles

With the wide selection of clothes now available, it is almost always possible to find something that is fashionable and, if necessary, concealing.

Sweaters and cardigans for men have replaced jackets for most occasional and informal wear. Tunic tops and Mexican style ponchos (which are made of an oblong or square piece of cloth with a slit in the middle for the head to go through), are worn by many girls, and together with a comfortable pair of slacks make a useful and attractive combination for wheelchair users.

The important thing for any woman with a disability, particularly if she is in a wheelchair, is to choose an eye-catching colour or a pretty pattern, rather than a particular style. A sweater knitted in a beautiful colour, or slacks and tunic with good colour co-ordination, will look more attractive than a tight fitting dress or blouse and skirt.

Underwear

Underwear should fit well but not too tightly. For the more severely disabled, or the person who is partially incontinent, cotton underwear is cooler and more absorbent to wear than man-made fibres.

Underpants can be attached to trousers with a strip of Velcro for ease of dressing and toileting. The Velcro is attached to the inside waistband of the trousers and the outside band of the pants and fastened. It is advisable to have a spare strip to fasten to the underpants when laundering so that the burrs will not pick up fluff from other garments.

Pants with a lengthened gusset which extends to the waistband for fastening will prove useful for those women who cannot reach a buttoned gusset, or manage with slip on pants. The gusset can be fastened at the waistband with hooks or Velcro.

Knickers or pants can be adapted for toilet purposes by splitting up the front and back seams and through the gusset. The top three or four inches on either side are then overlapped and sewn and the remaining opening bound with bias binding. The sides will fall into position when worn. This adaptation is best carried out on a garment one size bigger than usually worn.

Brassieres can be adapted by splitting the central front seam and sewing in large hooks and eyes, together with a strip of Velcro attached to a small length of tape for extra fastening. If the brassiere tends to ride up, elastic loops stitched to the band, and fastened by buttons to the girdle or pants will overcome this problem. Front fastening brassieres are available commercially, and shops selling this type of garment will usually obtain one on a special order if they do not carry a stock.

With the present fashion for step-in girdles, it may be difficult to obtain the side fastening type of corset that many elderly women prefer. Some proprietary corsets which fasten with a strap and hook can be individually measured and made up. This service is available in many of the larger towns. Sometimes the corsetiere who visits hospitals to make up surgical corsets will visit people at home.

If the younger disabled woman needs some form of girdle or corset, it is better to wear a small suspender belt with a side fastening rather than an elasticated pull on girdle which could prove difficult to put on. Another alternative is a light-weight pull on pantie corselette. This all in one garment combines both brassiere and corset and fastens at the crutch in the same style as cami-knickers.

Tights are now worn by many women, which dispenses with the need for a garment for holding suspenders. If difficulty is experienced in putting on tights it is advisable to sit on a small dining chair or a bed so that one has plenty of room for arm movements, and cross one leg over the other. If each leg of the tights is rolled down as far as the foot and pulled on each leg in turn as far as the knee it should be easier to finish pulling them on from a standing position or, if necessary, leaning against a wall for extra support.

Dressmaking

Standard dressmaking patterns can be adapted to suit individual requirements. Many people are able to learn the art of cutting a pattern to suit their needs, and provided that basic dressmaking principles are applied, it should not prove too difficult to adapt a pattern. The Association of Occupational Therapists have a very useful little booklet on this subject, which is available on request. (See p. 182 for the address.)

An adjustable dressmaker's model is invaluable, for once it has been fitted to the body contours all future fittings can take place on the model, thus saving tiring activity.

When selecting the style of pattern some of the following points may prove useful:

Necklines: Low cut necklines emphasise rather than flatter short women, and those with high waists and small rib cages.

Sleeves: Raglan or dolman type sleeves will provide more freedom of movement for the woman in a wheelchair.

Pockets: Should be positioned well forward on the garment and be easy to reach.

Fastenings: Velcro can replace buttons, zips, hooks and eyes, and it is easy to stitch to fabric for small or large openings.

Gussets and openings: Skilful use of gussets such as under the arm or in the crutch of trousers or slacks will be more comfortable, easier for movement, and for dressing.

Maternity type openings on skirts and slacks will be useful for the wheelchair user.

Back openings should be avoided when upper limb movement is restricted.

Waistlines: Elastic sewn in the back of the waistband of a skirt or slacks will help to achieve a fitted appearance and yet make dressing and undressing easier.

Skirts: Wrapover skirts continue to be fashionable and are a practical and easy style for many disabled women to wear. They can be made quite easily by the home dressmaker, provided that care is taken that the hem is even at the wrapover. Flared or A-line skirts are easier to wear than straight skirts and will keep their shape better.

Materials

The material chosen for any garment should be lightweight and warm, for the warmer the material the fewer the garments required, thus simplifying dressing and undressing. Those with a "sheen" tend to slide over one another easily, again simplifying dressing procedures. However, the wheelchair user may find that there is a tendency to slip forward when wearing this type of clothing.

Stretch materials add neatness and warmth when attached to collars and cuffs, but stretch socks, stockings and underpants are difficult for many people to wear because they have small openings which are difficult to locate.

Wool is relatively resilient and absorbent, but has the disadvantage that it will not stand up to frequent laundering unless great care is taken, and wool jersey must be dry-cleaned. Cotton underclothes are particularly useful for they can be boiled or bleached as necessary, and they are much cooler to wear than man-made fibres.

Many garments for both men and women are now made from Crimplene. This material is both warm and lightweight, washes well and dries quickly. It rarely needs ironing for it keeps its shape when washed and it is available in a variety of weights and weaves. Terylene is also easy to care for, and this is important for it is more economical if clothes can be laundered at home rather than dry-cleaned.

The colour and pattern of outer garments should also be carefully considered. Dark and sombre patterns have a depressing effect, as well as being difficult to keep free from spotting and fluff.

Specially designed clothing

Some firms are now designing and making clothes, such as dresses and nightwear, specially for disabled people. Many of these garments have specially designed openings for easier dressing. The styles are quite attractive and colourful and are suitable for a wide range of ages and sizes.

CASE HISTORIES

Miss H is a buyer at a large department store and leads a busy and active life. For the past three or four years she has had osteoarthritis in her left hip with increasing pain and stiffness in the joint.

She lives in a small flat which was already planned as labour saving, and she gradually adapted her routine and bought one or two useful household tools, such as a long handled dustpan and brush, to ease her housework problems and save the pain involved in bending and kneeling.

Her main problem, however, was dressing, and she was finding it painful and difficult to reach her left foot to get clothes on over her feet, and to put on her shoes and stockings. Her doctor

Front opening nightdress with wrapover back

suggested that she should see the domiciliary occupational therapist, who called at Miss H's flat to look into the difficulties.

Three aids solved her dressing problems : a long handled shoe horn, a stocking aid or stocking gutter, and a long handled pick-up reacher. With the reacher she was able to position her pants and girdle over her left foot and pull them up within reach of her hands without bending her left hip. It also proved a useful aid around the flat for picking things up from the floor and she was supplied with a second one to keep in her office.

She has since had an operation to have her arthritic hip replaced with an artificial one. This was very successful and she is now free from pain and full movement is returning. Two months after the operation she no longer needed the stocking aid and shoe horn, but the long handled reacher continues to be her most useful tool.

Two years after Mr. G retired, he had a stroke and was partially paralysed down one side of his body. He was in hospital for four weeks and then he returned home. By that time he was able to walk a little with the aid of a quadruped stick, and he attended the rehabilitation department every afternoon during the week following his discharge from hospital so that he could be shown how to regain his independence.

His main difficulty was in dressing himself. This was partly due to his poor balance, especially if he bent down, and partly because his arm was recovering very slowly and he had some spasticity in this limb.

Aids and gadgets tend to confuse people who have had a stroke, but a few simple changes in Mr. G's routine and methods proved to be a great help.

He learnt to dress sitting on the edge of the bed with his feet firmly on the ground and with his weaker side towards the bed-head and supported by the pillows. His clothes were laid on a chair in the order in which he had to put them on—his shirt first, then underpants and trousers, followed by pullover, then socks and shoes. His shirt sleeve was drawn up over his weaker hand and arm and worked well up over his elbow before his stronger arm was put in, and the shirt was then pulled over his head. A nylon sports shirt was found most convenient for everyday use, and when more formal clothes were needed, his wife and son gave him some help in the early days.

To put garments over his feet safely, his weak leg was lifted and put up on a chair seat, or crossed over the good knee. Underpants and trousers were put over the foot and pulled up to the knee, the braces were then looped over the weaker arm to keep the trousers in place while the good leg was put through the pants and trouser legs. (If possible, the trousers should be worked up over the buttocks by rolling the seat from side to side on the bed before standing to adjust the braces and fasten the trousers.)

It was necessary for Mr. G to rest before putting on his pull-over, and he then put his foot upon the chair to put on his socks and slip-on shoes.

He needed plenty of time and a quiet place to relearn his dressing skills—and a very patient wife.

6

Eating and Drinking

MANY physically disabled people, particularly those who live alone, or are left alone for long periods, tend to neglect their diet. They may have difficulties in purchasing, preparing and eating their food. Furthermore, their relative inactivity does not stimulate a good appetite, or they may be forced for financial reasons to economize on food.

The local authority social services may well be able to help and advise on the overall difficulties of eating and drinking. This advice includes the furniture required for feeding, the implements used (crockery, cutlery, and the other aids required by those who are unable to use conventional tableware) and the most suitable food or diet.

Furniture

Access to the dining room or dining area, the approach to the table, and the most convenient type of chair may be a major problem for the person with limited walking ability, stiff hips and knees, and the person in a wheelchair. Modern houses are often small, and the extra space needed for manoeuvring a wheelchair or walking frame can only be obtained by reducing the amount of furniture in the room. Modern tables and chairs are often too low and flimsy in construction, and the tables do not provide adequate clearance, especially for the person in a wheelchair. The person with stiff hips and knees will need a high dining table, and this can be achieved by standing the table on blocks of wood. Old-fashioned kitchen or dining tables often give better leg clearance and also act as a support for getting up and down, or walking round the room. The position of the table in the room is important. If it is placed against a wall or in a corner, it is particularly suitable as a support when getting in and out of the chair. If it is necessary to alter the height of the dining chair, it can be done in the same way as the table. Old-fashioned high backed dining chairs are often more comfortable than those with a low back.

Desk or domestic arms can be fitted to a wheelchair so that it is possible to make a close approach to the table, or a tray can be attached to the wheelchair. Cantilever tables often prove useful when it is not possible to sit at the dining table. But it is important that if using one of these alternative methods the wheelchair should be placed adjacent to the table where the other members of the family are sitting, so that there is no sense of isolation from conversation.

For those with uncontrolled, inco-ordinated movements or spasm, heavy old fashioned furniture is more stable than many of the modern designs. A further problem for these people is the likelihood of spills with food and drink. Formica topped tables, plastic tablecloths and PVC upholstery on chairs make cleaning easier.

Crockery and cutlery

A wide variety of eating and drinking aids, suitable for people with weakness or deformity of the hands and arms, is available, including cutlery, non-slip table mats and trays, specially designed cups, plates and drinking straws.

Conventional cutlery can sometimes be adapted for use by those with a weak or stiff grip by enlarging the handles with sponge or rubber tubing attached to the implement with Velcro. It is also possible to lengthen and shape the handles of conventional cutlery with metal or wood to enable people with weak arms and hands to get the food to their mouths without assistance.

Most hospital and local authority occupational therapy departments have many methods of adapting cutlery to suit individual requirements.

Dual purpose cutlery, such as Nelson knives (or cheese knives), will serve as both knife and fork for the one-handed person. Cutting is achieved by a rocking motion with the blade, and the prong is used to pick up the food, but it is not advisable for anyone with weakness, inco-ordination or tremor to use this method.

Sporks, which are shaped like pickle spoons, and cake forks

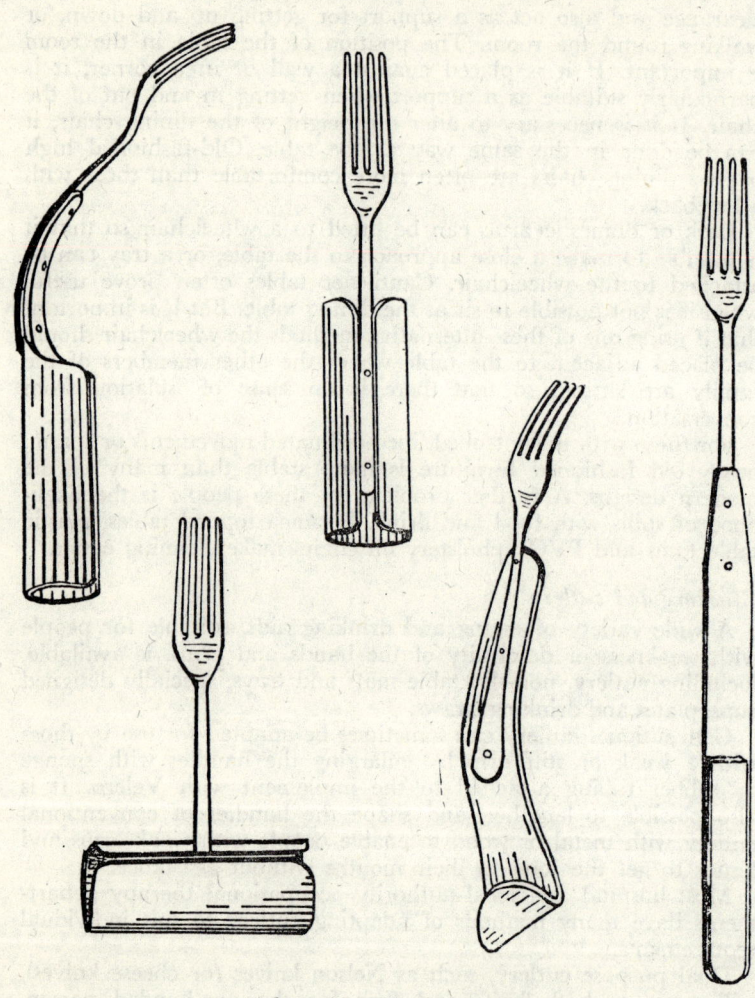

Adapted handles for cutlery

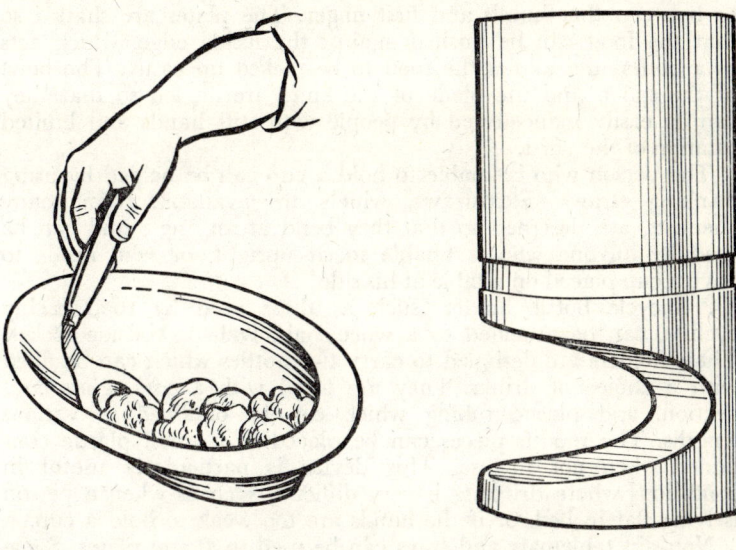

Manoy tableware: plate and beaker

can also be used for the dual purpose of cutting and lifting some foods.

Many people have difficulty in keeping food on the plate, particularly when using only one hand. There are plastic guards which clip on to the plate, but it is not easy to keep them clean, and although helpful they are not very efficient. Because of these deficiencies, a special range of crockery and cutlery, the Manoy range, has been designed in Melaware. The problems of feeding and drinking are interlinked, and a complete crockery and cutlery set has been produced. The main feature of the goblet shaped cup is the lack of a "handle" which can be difficult for an arthritic or weak hand to grip, therefore the cut-away stem was designed so that it can be lifted by the palm of the hand, one or both hands, or between the thumb and first finger. The plates are shaped so that the food can be pushed against the inside edge, which acts as a buffer and allows the food to be picked up easily. The bowl of the spoon and the blade of the knife are angled so that they can be easily manoeuvred by people with stiff hands and limited rotation of the wrist.

The person who is unable to hold a cup can be helped by using drinking straws. Flexistraws, which are available from many chemists, are designed so that they bend at an angle and can be used by anyone who is unable to sit upright, or who needs to have a cup placed on a table at his side.

A bicycle bottle holder, such as those used by road racing cyclists, can be attached to a wheelchair, wall or bedside locker. These holders are designed to carry two bottles which can be filled with a choice of drinks. They are fitted with a cork, glass connection, and plastic tubing which can be obtained in various lengths. The mouth pieces can be placed in a small plastic container when not in use. This device is particularly useful in conditions where drinking is very difficult, such as when a person is lying flat in bed, or if the hands are too weak to hold a cup.

Non-slip tablemats and trays can be used to secure plates. Some of these are commercially available, but plastic foam sheets, pimpled rubber, or Copydex painted to the underside of plates and bowls and allowed to dry will also prevent slipping.

Food and diet

Many disabled people tend to have poor appetites, and one should aim to provide a good well balanced diet with plenty of fresh vegetables, fruit, fish, cheese and meat. These are the main foods which supply the necessary vitamin intake for a healthy body, and although food prices are high, one should aim to include as many of them as possible in the diet. If there is a tendency to overweight due to inactivity, the fattening foods, such as potatoes, rice, bread, cakes and puddings, should all be avoided. It is very important for anyone with a physical disability which limits movement to avoid excess weight, for this will add to mobility and transfer problems, placing greater strain on the arms and shoulders, particularly if using a walking aid.

If eating is difficult, try to provide food that is easy to pick up and chew. Salads, which are well shredded and mixed with oil or salad cream, can be eaten with a spoon. Meat should be cut up into small pieces or minced, and vegetables mashed or diced so that it is unnecessary to use a knife. Soup can be served in a two-handled cup or a soup cup so that it can be drunk straight from the cup, without using a spoon. Some of the thicker soups contain vegetables and meat and are very useful for a mid-day snack. Tinned foods, such as those given to toddlers, may be suitable for patients with small appetites, for they are easy to heat and serve. (The preparation of food is dealt with in Chapter 8.)

The presentation of food on the plate is very important for if it is appetizingly arranged it will be an encouragement to eat. This applies just as much to the person who needs someone to feed him, as to the person who is able to feed himself.

Case History

Pauline is spastic (cerebral palsy), the fourth child in a very happy family. She is now six and walks with a spastic staggering gait and has some difficulty in controlling the movements of her arms and hands. She also has a slight problem in swallowing and controlling her saliva.

Pauline was becoming very upset that she needed help at meal-times, and when she tried to feed herself she often spilled the food or knocked over her cup. The harder she tried the more attention was focussed on her efforts and the more difficult she found it to control her right arm and hand.

Attendance at the occupational therapy department in her local hospital gave her mother some useful ideas to try at home. A large Manoy plate was fixed firmly to the table with an octopus suction disc bought at a large chain store chemist; the handle of her spoon was pushed into a length of rubazote (rubber tubing) to give an enlarged grip (this can be removed easily for washing). A baby mug with a weighted bottom was tried at first, and Pauline soon progressed from this to using a full-size double handled beaker obtained through the Spastics Society. The occupational therapist made a weighted cuff from soft webbing, fastened with Velcro and with small flat lead weights slotted into it. This helped to damp down and control the unwanted movements of Pauline's right hand. Simple exercises are helping to control her saliva problem; these are preceded by sucking small lumps of ice as an aid to swallowing, and the exercises include blowing a whistle, blowing bubbles through a polythene straw, blowing a table tennis ball along, and trying to pick up the ball by sucking at it through a straw. Pauline's mother and her brothers and sisters have thought of many other helpful "games."

Although she is still very slow at mealtimes, Pauline is now able to feed herself.

7

Home-making and Housework

HOME is an expression of a woman's character, and although all the members of the family contribute to it, it is the wife and mother who influences it the most. The disabled homemaker will naturally have to face more problems than an able-bodied housewife, but a lot will depend upon the severity of her disability.

The housewife with a gradual onset of handicap will learn to adapt herself to the changes as they take place, learning new techniques of tackling each difficulty as it arises. When the disability has been of long duration, from childhood or adolescence, the woman has learned her own abilities and limitations and will only need to re-assess as particular circumstances change, such as when she marries, has children, moves house, goes out to work as well as running her home. In general, if the family are used to having a mother with physical disability they adapt and grow up with the pattern. Sudden onset of disability however, often imposes considerable strain on the whole family and it is necessary to plan the support necessary to cope with the new situation. In favourable conditions, the adaptations and changes in patterns of living will be accepted both by the disabled member of the family and the other members, and it is possible to plan for maximum independence for the housewife with a physical disability. However, when there is impairment of intellectual capacity then the overall level of independence may well be restricted.

All disabled homemakers will be affected by habits and traditions, and by their personal attitudes towards housework. Some people love homemaking and make it a full time occupation, while others wish to get it done quickly so they have more time for other things.

When planning housework, allowance must be made for the housewife to have a rest period during the day, so that she is not too tired to enjoy her leisure time with the rest of the family in the evening. It is also advisable to plan a regular set of jobs for husband and children so that they will know what is expected of them, rather than requesting their assistance at short notice, when they may have planned to do something else.

If disablement is new, it may be helpful to carry out a job

analysis for a few weeks and keep notes in a diary to see how the plan is working out, which jobs are piling up and which jobs can be cut down. Some people prefer to clean through the house quickly every day and have a really good clean up at the weekends. This may prove more practical if help is available at weekends. The washing of the family's clothes could also take place once a week using a washing machine, if there is help available, but if it is preferred to keep the housework and the washing down to manageable proportions single-handed, then certain jobs should be planned for specific days.

When help is available, it should be directed towards the things that the disabled woman *cannot* do. Home Helps are usually given these instructions but privately employed domestic help may not recognise the problems and will need specific instructions regarding floor cleaning, windows, high dusting, stairs, polishing and laundry. In some cases, they may also undertake household shopping.

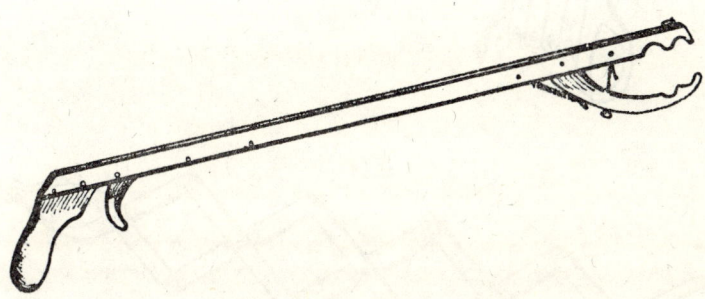

"Pick-up" stick, or long arm reacher

Aids

One of the most useful pieces of equipment for a disabled housewife, or any disabled person, is a pick-up stick. This is a "tool" very similar in size and shape to a walking stick, with a metal jaw at one end and a pinch-grip mechanism at the other. Squeezing the lever attached to the handle will open the jaws to pick up an object which may be lying on the floor or a shelf or some other inaccessible place, the lever is then released to grip the object and transfer it to its destination, where the jaws are again opened by the same method and the object released. Pick-up sticks can be used for work in the kitchen, for housework, dressing and leisure activities—in fact for any job where it is necessary to pick things up and avoid bending, reaching or stretching. There are a number of different models available but they all work on the same principle. Pick-up sticks can be obtained from occupational therapy departments, or the British Red Cross Society.

When items need to be moved from room to room, a small trolley will save unnecessary journeys for it can carry all the cleaning materials such as dusters, polishes, sponges, wastepaper basket, and any other items needed for housecleaning. An apron with big pockets to hold some of the cleaning materials is also useful. A small bag or basket attached to a walking frame enables items to be carried easily and leave the hands free.

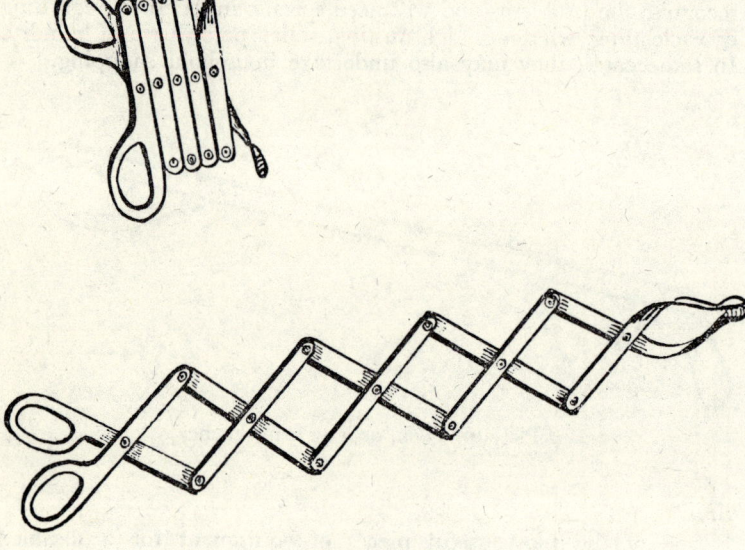

Lazy tongs

Although a few pieces of multi-purpose equipment are more useful than many single-purpose ones, it is likely that the disabled housewife will benefit more from mechanized aids than the able-bodied housewife. She will therefore need plenty of accessible storage space for the various pieces of equipment, and plenty of electric sockets which should be sited about thirty inches from floor level, so that they are easy to reach.

A kitchen stool will help to prevent fatigue when ironing, preparing vegetables or washing up. The height of the stool is important and it should be neither too high nor too low. It is better to buy one that is too high and cut the legs to a convenient height

High kitchen trolley, walking and carrying aid.
Note lower shelf cut back for knee space

or, if bending at the hips is difficult, the legs should be cut shorter at the front so that it can be used for "perching" on, rather than sitting. If the stool is fitted with a back support, this will also help to prevent tiredness. Some housewives have castors fitted on to a kitchen chair, or on to a low stool such as those used in shoe shops, so that they can "scoot" round the kitchen.

Housewives who use a walking aid may find that a wheelchair will help them to cope with the housework more easily. Whether propelled by hand in the conventional manner, punted with sticks, or paddled with the feet, it leaves the hands free for working. Whether a wheelchair will increase functional capability or not, can be assessed in the local hospital occupational therapy department, or the domiciliary occupational therapist may be able to loan a wheelchair on a trial basis.

Furniture and fittings

The management of the home will be made much easier if furnishings, furniture and fittings are designed to save work. Patterned fabrics and floor coverings show less marks, and dirty footmarks in kitchen and sitting rooms will be avoided if shoes are changed for house-shoes or slippers in the hall or lobby. Stretch covers on upholstered furniture can be removed for regular washing. Non-iron sheets and pillow cases, and small towels rather than large ones will be easier to wash and dry. Wall to wall carpeting is easier to clean than linoleum or polished floors, and small rugs are difficult to keep free from dust. Vinyl flooring in kitchen and bathroom can be cleaned easily with a long handled squeezee mop.

Housecleaning

Housecleaning generally is very heavy work, and it may be too difficult for the person with weak arms, stiff knees, or who uses a wheelchair. But many people who are disabled manage to run their homes efficiently with the adoption of new techniques and some aids, needing help only occasionally for some of the heavier tasks.

Holding a duster may be painful for arthritic hands, and a mitten made of dust-attracting material may be easier to use than a conventional duster. Other people may find that a small hand mop which is impregnated with polish will make the task easier. Polished or gloss-painted surfaces do not hold much dust, and a polyurethane varnish on some surfaces may dispense with the need to polish. If ornaments and other objects on shelves are kept to a minimum then dusting will be less difficult.

Long handled equipment for floor cleaning will dispense with the need to kneel. Squeezee mops, mops with long flexible handles, long handled dustpans and brushes, carpet sweepers and vacuum cleaners can all be used from the standing or sitting position.

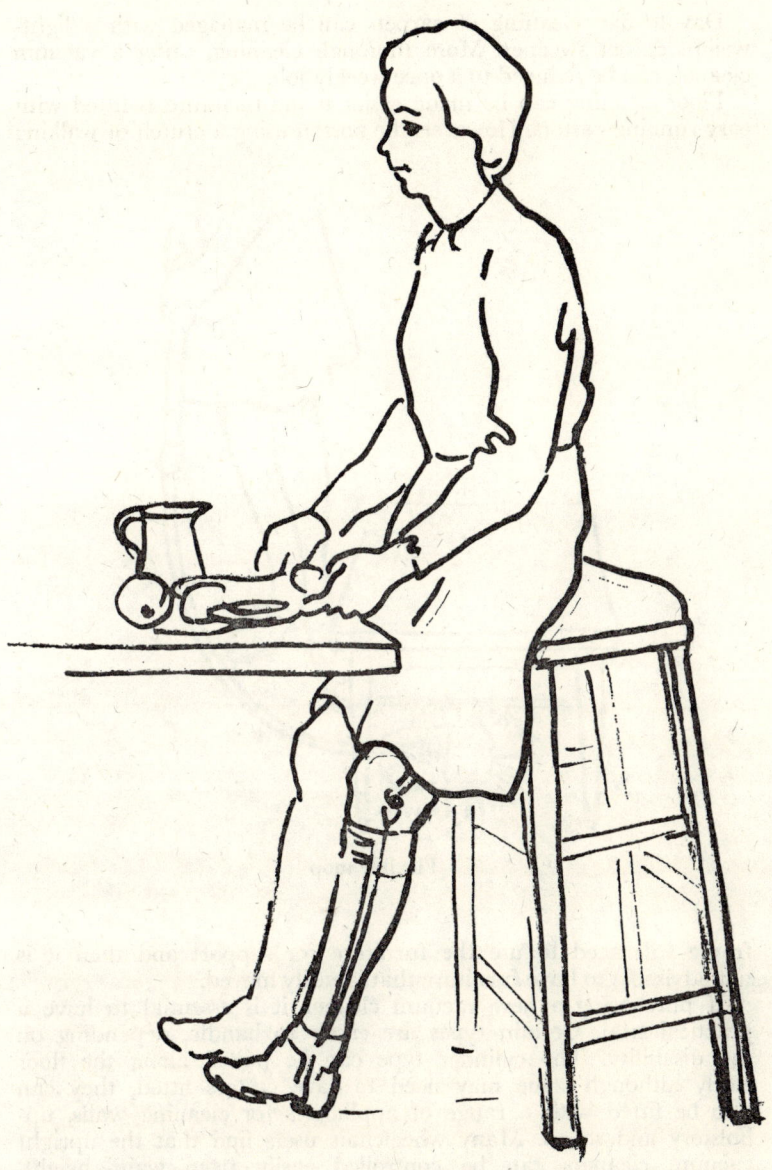

Kitchen stool with $1\frac{1}{2}$ to 2 ins. cut off front legs to make comfortable seat for person with stiff knees, hips and spine. Rubber tips on the legs of the stool will give extra stability

Day to day cleaning of carpets can be managed with a light-weight carpet sweeper. More thorough cleaning, using a vacuum cleaner, can be reduced to a once weekly job.

Floor cleaning can be made easier if the furniture is fitted with easy running castors. However, the person using a crutch or walking

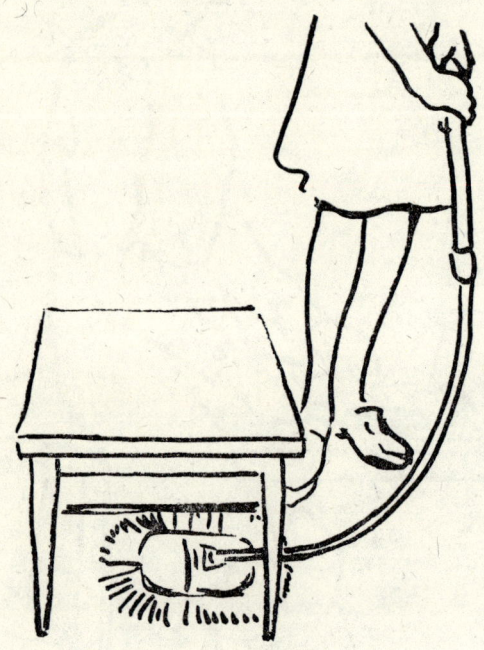

Flexible mop

frame will need to use the furniture for support and then it is not advisable to have furniture that is easily moved.

If purchasing a new vacuum cleaner it is essential to have a practical trial. Certain types are easier to handle, depending on the disability. The cylinder type can be pulled along the floor easily although some may need to have castors fitted, they can also be fitted with a range of appliances for cleaning walls, upholstery and so on. Many wheelchair users find that the upright vacuum cleaners can be controlled easily from waist height. Suction power is greater on some models than on others and it is advisable to try them on different types of carpet. If hands are weak, it may be possible to clip the hose of the cylinder type to

Long handled dustpan and brush

a belt around the waist, leaving the hands free to move the nozzle with little effort. Some of the machines have easy to empty dust-bags.

Stairs are difficult for a disabled person to clean, but the treads can be wiped with a moist sponge or cloth from a sitting position on the stairs. Bath-cleaning is another problem, but water softener in the bath reduces soap scum, and if each person cleans the bath after use it should not require too much attention. Long handled mops and sponges are useful for cleaning the bathroom floor.

Window cleaning

Windows at ground floor level can be cleaned with the aid of a small sponge on a handle, which is specifically designed for this purpose and obtainable from most hardware shops. They can then

Easy-reach window mop

be polished with a duster held in a pick-up stick. However, it is usually preferable for most of the window cleaning to be done by another member of the family, or a window cleaner.

Bedmaking

This strenuous activity involves bending, lifting, stretching and shaking to make the bed properly. Modern bedlinen is now designed to make the task easier, with crease resistant sheets, fitted corners, lightweight blankets, and continental quilts or duvets. Strain on the back can be avoided by making the bed from a kneeling position, and some people find that a stool which has been fitted with easy running castors can be used to scoot round the bed. If there are several layers of bedclothes it is better to handle them singly laying them over a chair at the foot of the bed, they can then be drawn up all at one side and then at the other, making only one journey round the bed necessary. Tucking in the bedclothes is another problem encountered by people with arthritic hands, and a wooden spade can be used for this purpose.

Re-making the bed with clean bed-linen is difficult for the person with weak hands and arms, but if the sheets are folded across the bed, instead of the traditional length-wise fashion, they are easier to manage. When changing a pillow case, the pillow may be held under the chin leaving the hands free to position the pillow case. Nylon sheets and pillow cases are easier to handle because they are more slippery.

Laundry

If laundry is to be done at home, the most valuable piece of equipment for the disabled housewife is a spin drier, for it will cope with the difficult process of handling heavy wet clothes, and also make it easier to dry them.

If a washing machine is to be purchased, a twin-tub machine incorporating a spin drier, or a fully automatic machine will reduce laundry handling to the minimum. Some fully automatic machines need to be plumbed into the water supply, and are rather extravagant with hot water, but they do reduce work to the absolute minimum. Some of the automatic machines are front loading and although this may be more suitable for the woman in a wheelchair, it may be difficult for people who cannot bend. It is important to give the machines a practical trial before purchasing to ensure that the controls can easily be reached.

Drying the washing also gives rise to problems, and coping with an outside washing line may be difficult. If a clothes line is used it should not be fixed so high that it is necessary to reach, and a clothes prop should be available. Rotary clothes lines are easier to use than a long clothes line down a garden path.

It may be more practical to dry clothes indoors, especially if a spin drier is used. An electrically heated drying cabinet with removable wooden rods dries clothes very quickly. Alternatively, a nylon clothes line which is attached to the wall in a container, to which it can be returned when not in use, is very effective if used in a bathroom. Indoor rotary lines which hang from the ceiling, and plastic covered wire racks which fold back against the wall when not in use, are other alternatives. Indeed, the old-fashioned clothes-airer in the kitchen may be more practical than hanging clothes outside to dry.

Transporting wet laundry is a problem which can be solved by using a specially designed trolley which has a plastic bag or bucket attached.

Ironing should be done on a stable, adjustable board, which is easy to erect and dismantle. A conventional ironing board could have the stand removed and be attached to the wall with hinges and folding supports. This makes it easy to assemble, and easy to use, because it will provide leg room for the person sitting in a wheelchair or on a stool.

The type of iron used is also important. The ideal weight should be between $3\frac{1}{2}$ and 4 lbs, and it is a mistake to assume that a heavy iron is better for removing the creases, for it is the heat and the slight dampness of the clothes which produce a good finish. If clothes do get too dry then a liquid container with a small nozzle, such as a used washing-up liquid bottle, filled with clean water, can be used for damping them. Nylon, terylene, and other drip-dry materials, underwear, nightwear, towels and teatowels do not need ironing if they are folded directly they are dry. Provided they are well aired it is not necessary to expend further energy on them.

Shopping

Shopping is an important social activity which encourages a potentially isolated person to make and keep local contacts. Whenever possible, the disabled housewife should do her own shopping. If she is able to manage alone a two wheeled shopping trolley can be used, or a shoulder bag which will enable her to carry a few purchases at a time, and also leave her hands free. Some people find that getting money from a purse is difficult and small change cannot be seen in a conventional type of purse. It may be helpful if a small tray-shaped purse is used, for this opens in such a fashion that the money can easily be seen and handled.

Small local shops often provide a friendly and personal service which cannot always be found in supermarkets. A chair is often provided in these smaller shops and time allowed for selection of purchases. This may well be the best type of shopping for the elderly housewife or the young woman with no family, but when catering for a larger number of people it is usually better to shop at a supermarket (preferably during the early part of the week when they are not so busy), and to arrange for a friend, husband or an elder child to come along to help select the goods and carry the shopping home. In the larger branches of some supermarkets the staff are specially trained and may be able to help with the selection of purchases, but this is not the case in all stores.

It is important for the family to understand that the mother should be encouraged and given the facilities, if possible, to do the family shopping. It is always frustrating for the housewife who is unable to see for herself what is available in the shops and the current market prices and bargains.

If it is impossible to go shopping, and there is no one who can help, orders can often be telephoned to local shops with a delivery service. Mobile shops are also useful in rural areas and in some of the suburbs of large towns, for they will call regularly for orders once contact has been established.

Case History

Mrs. H, a teacher and a widow with two young children, injured her back when bending to lift a heavy object from the floor. She had a severe attack of pain and was advised to wear a plaster jacket for several weeks. During this time she had to reorganize her home management to reduce to a minimum the strain on her back. At the hospital she was advised on the techniques to avoid bending, stretching and lifting with a bent back, and was also given some aids to help her to avoid harmful movements.

She had already discovered that a firm chair was more comfortable than a soft one, but she had not considered using a chair in the kitchen to give support to her back whilst washing up or preparing vegetables. She found that an office chair could be set at the right height for the job, and she rested her feet on a box when necessary. Making cakes and baking activities generally were very tiring, and she tried to keep this to a minimum while she saved for an electric food mixer.

She installed more wall cupboards in her kitchen, with sliding doors, and kept the most frequently used utensils, crockery and foodstuffs in them. A friend helped her by fixing storage baskets to the hinged doors of her floor standing cupboards, so that the contents were more easily accessible. To extend her range of reach without stretching she used a long arm reacher, with which she also picked things up from the floor, reached the tops of the curtains, and dusted the picture rails.

She learnt to bend her knees rather than her back, and lifted only when it was absolutely essential, and then only with a straight back. She knelt to bath the children and to clean the bath, using long handled sponges and brushes.

She had a twin-tub washing machine, but lifting the wet clothes, especially sheets, from one tub to the other was a strain unless she braced her back, keeping her elbows at her sides and lifted by using only her forearms. When possible she did small amounts at a time, although this was rather extravagant with water and soap. She sometimes used the launderette which had front loading machines, and she transported the washed clothes on her shopping trolley to the dryer. At home she had a rotary clothes line close to the path and near the back door, and used a laundry trolley to hold a plastic basket at a comfortable height when taking

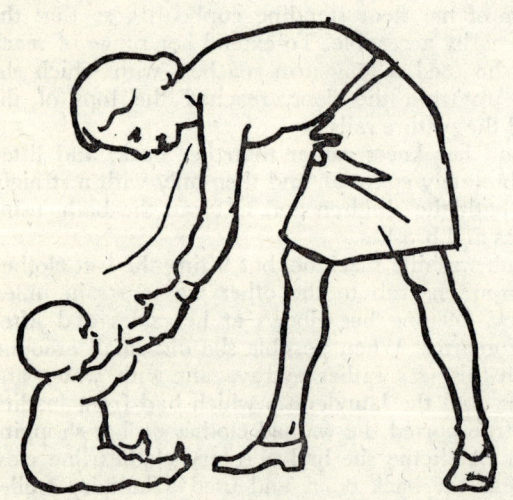

Lifting methods: right (top) and wrong

clothes out to the line. As clothes and household linen wore out she replaced with as much easy-care linen as possible.

Her ironing board was excellent because it had a wide range of height adjustment and she could sit on a swivel chair when ironing, taking the garment from the pile, ironing it, then swivelling the other way to fold it, and place it on the pile for airing.

The children were taught to pick up their toys from the floor, and to be tidy in their bedrooms, but of course the floors had to be cleaned. The kitchen and bathroom were mopped using a squeezee mop and liquid polish, and occasionally a friend came to help her and gave the floors a thorough scrubbing. Mrs. H had always used a cylinder vacuum cleaner but now found it was too heavy to lift and she exchanged it for an upright model which she found easier to manoeuvre.

Bed-making was a source of strain, and Mrs. H converted some of her sheets to fitted corners, by sewing a mitre at one end, and stitching on elastic so that the sheets stayed in place at the bottom of the bed and there was less tucking in to do. Rather than have the beds standing on blocks so that they were a comfortable height for bedmaking, which she felt would spoil the look of the bedroom, she knelt to make the beds. Her daughters are being taught to help with making the beds, but Mrs H is saving to buy continental quilts for all the beds which will solve many of the bedmaking problems.

She has her own car, which was chosen for its particularly firm, upright seat, and shops daily on her way home from school, so that she never has to carry a heavy shopping bag. She uses a shopping trolley in the supermarket, and puts the shopping in two plastic bags so that she carries an even weight, and can manage to put the shopping into the car more easily and take it out when she gets home.

Injured backs tend to have exacerbations of pain and discomfort, and it is necessary constantly to guard against activities which may produce another attack of severe pain.

8

Kitchen

MOST women's magazines, cookery books, and domestic science books give very good advice about kitchen design and layout, but some particular aspects are important for people who have a physical disability.

Firstly, there is likely to be a major difference between the requirements of a woman who has a wheelchair all the time, and one who, although disabled, does not use a wheelchair in the house. Sometimes however, it might be wise for a partially disabled woman (or man for that matter), to use a wheelchair for kitchen activities. It may be much safer and quicker to work sitting down and propel the wheelchair with the feet thus leaving the hands free, or use a wheelchair tray to carry necessary utensils and materials about. Safety is of such importance to anyone who is suffering from weakness or inco-ordination of movements that the use of a wheelchair as a safety factor and increased aid to mobility, should always be remembered.

For those who do not use a wheelchair, the long, narrow galley type of kitchen is probably the best arrangement. In this design everything is close at hand, and surfaces are available for support and stability.

The woman using a wheelchair all the time does present problems in the general design of her kitchen, and the style of the fitments. Ideally, the requirements are a large square kitchen, plenty of manoeuvring space, a corner sink with knee space underneath fitments with recesses at the base to accommodate the footrests of the wheelchair, and storage space that can be reached easily from a sitting position.

A continuous, adequate work surface, of the correct height to eliminate unnecessary lifting, and with a sink and split level cooker on the same run is the ideal arrangement. The order of procedures and the relationship between sink, cooker, table and refrigerator, should all be carefully considered, so that energy is not wasted on backtracking. The kitchen table will provide an additional work surface and reduce journeys in the kitchen area.

In some houses, particularly those built at the beginning of this century, the combination of kitchen-dining room provides an

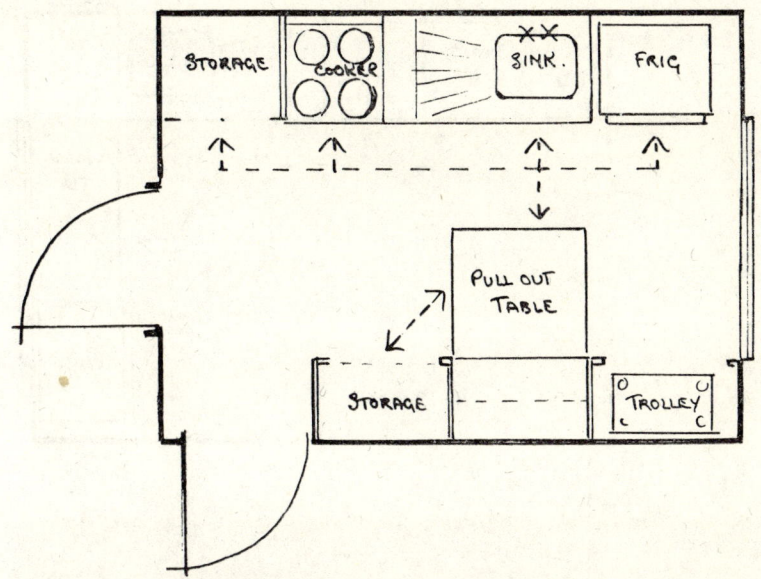

Kitchen for walking disabled housewife. Work routes are compact and labour saving. The hot pan can slide from cooker to sink and the table can be reached from the sink

ideal arrangement for the disabled housewife, for it reduces the need to carry crockery from one room to another. However, these big combined rooms may prove to be awkward unless altered, because the siting of the sink, door and windows is often inconvenient. Such a room, for example, usually has a deep sink under the window which is too deep for the woman in a wheelchair to use, and the window cannot be reached.

To reduce wheelchair manoeuvring, a corner sink, with working top leading to a split level cooker on one side, and a working top with access to a cupboard on the other, is probably an ideal arrangement.

Another way of reducing the amount of walking or manoeuvring in the kitchen is by installing a hatch from kitchen to dining room. Work surfaces and tables should be near the hatch on *both* sides.

Storage cupboards often present problems, but by careful organisation, entailing the separation of items used regularly from those used only occasionally, and the separation of items used by non-disabled members of the family, many of the storage problems can be overcome.

In general, it is better to avoid deep shelves which are difficult

79

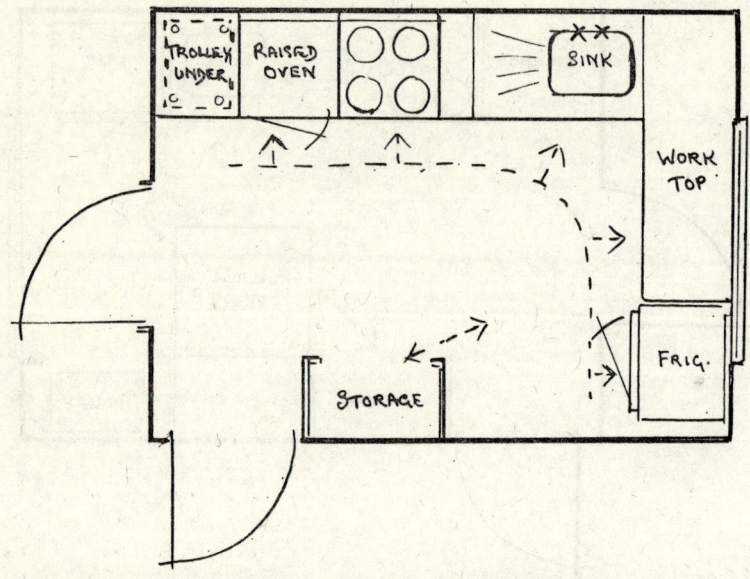

Kitchen for the housewife in a wheelchair. There is clear floor space for manoeuvring and the work routes are on an arc. The cooker is split level and there is knee space under the working surfaces

to reach into, and to use wire trays and racks which can be pulled forward. A stop should be provided so that they cannot fall off the runners. The inside of the cupboard doors can also be used for racks to hold bottles, cans and other small items.

A storage cupboard for household cleaning equipment can be made quite easily by a home handyman. Pull out trays and drawers holding dusters and polishes should be placed at a convenient height. A recess to hold the vacuum cleaner, together with clips on the cupboard door for mops, brooms, and vacuum cleaner hose and tools, will make it possible to reach all the household cleaning tools easily.

The amount of space required for food storage is related to the shopping method chosen. If it is done weekly, a refrigerator and a deep freeze are great assets, and generous cupboard space is essential. If shopping is done on a day to day basis less space will be required.

Equipment

The range of kitchen equipment available is wide and varied in design, and it may be better to select a few multi-purpose utensils

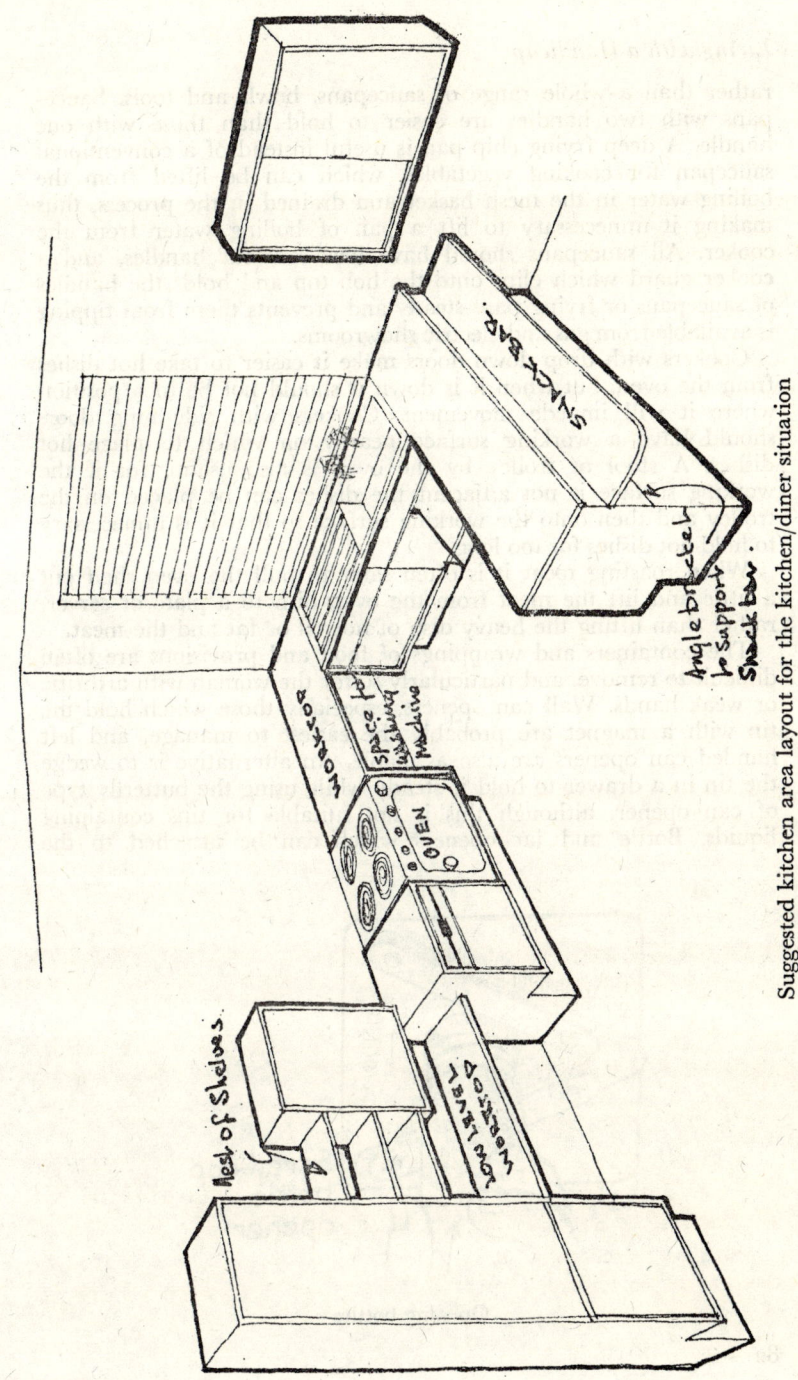

SNACK BAR

Angle Bracket to support Snack bar.

WORKTOP

space for washing machine

OVEN

WORKTOP

LOW LEVEL

Nest of shelves

Suggested kitchen area layout for the kitchen/diner situation

rather than a whole range of saucepans, bowls and tools. Saucepans with two handles are easier to hold than those with one
handle. A deep frying chip pan is useful instead of a conventional
saucepan for cooking vegetables, which can be lifted from the
boiling water in the mesh basket and drained in the process, thus
making it unnecessary to lift a pan of boiling water from the
cooker. All saucepans should have heat-resistant handles, and a
cooker guard which clips onto the hob top and holds the handles
of saucepans or frying pans steady and prevents them from tipping
is available from gas and electric showrooms.

Cookers with drop down doors make it easier to take hot dishes
from the oven, but when it is down it should not be in a position
where it will impede movement. Cookers with side-hung doors
should have a working surface nearby on which to place hot
dishes. A stool or trolley by the oven is also useful, for if the
working surface is not adjacent the dishes can be placed on the
trolley and then onto the working surface so that it is unnecessary
to hold hot dishes for too long.

When roasting meat it is often safer to pull the oven shelf out
a little and lift the meat from the oven dish to a plate or server,
rather than lifting the heavy dish of hot oil or fat and the meat.

The containers and wrappings of food and provisions are often
difficult to remove, and particularly so for the woman with arthritic
or weak hands. Wall can openers, especially those which hold the
tin with a magnet are probably the easiest to manage, and left
handed can openers are also available. An alternative is to wedge
the tin in a drawer to hold it steady while using the butterfly type
of can opener, although this is not suitable for tins containing
liquids. Bottle and jar openers which can be attached to the

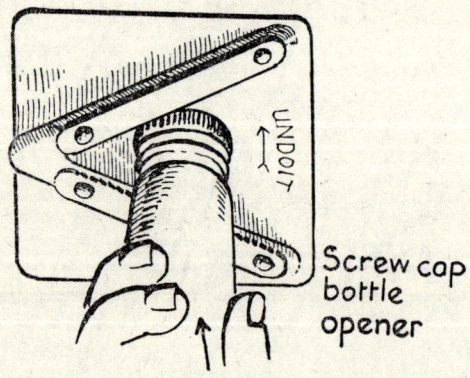

Screw cap
bottle
opener

Opening bottles

underside of a shelf and hold the top steady while the bottle or jar is turned are also useful. Plastic and foil wrapped food is best opened with a small vegetable knife with a serrated edge, or a pointed pair of scissors.

Another similar problem is that of controlling containers such as bowls and basins that slip when mixing or stirring in them. A mat of pimpled rubber, Dycem non-slip mats, multi-suction pads available from hardware shops, will hold them steady.

Prepacked foods, such as cake and pastry mixes, dispense with the need to do many of the mixing and stirring jobs associated with home baking. Pastry mixed without water and sprinkled over the tops of fruit and meat dishes forms a crumble when cooked and tastes just as good. The one stage method of cake making by placing all the ingredients in a bowl together and mixing with a wooden spoon or food mixer, is another labour and time saver.

A good hand mixer is an essential piece of equipment for the disabled housewife and there is a wide range, from very light one handed ones, to more sturdy ones which require two handed use. Handles are set square or off-set, and should be tried before purchasing because one type may be more suitable and comfortable to use than another. A pastry blender for rubbing fat into flour which dispenses with the fine hand movements necessary for blending pastry, is very comfortable and easy to use for the person with arthritic hands or the person who is one handed. These are available from most hardware shops. Many people with deformed or weak hands cannot manage the handles of a conventional rolling pin. They may be able to roll out the pastry with a simple wooden cylinder about two inches in diameter and twelve inches long, using the palms of their hands to roll it.

Food mixers are available in a wide price range, and the larger ones can be bought with attachments which help in most food preparation, such as mixing, blending, chopping, mincing, shredding, and liquidising.

Vegetable preparation is often difficult for the person with weak or stiff hands. Peelers can be obtained for left- or right-handed use, or with a transverse blade which is drawn towards the user so that the whole hand is used instead of the wrist action required by the others. A peeler can also be clamped to the side of the sink and the vegetable moved on it, instead of the tool being moved on the vegetable. It may be easier to remove the peel with a fine grater and a small hose attached to the tap so that the peel is washed away as it is grated off. Potatoes can be boiled or baked in their skins, provided they have been scrubbed beforehand.

There are several automatic choppers, but they require strength to use and the jarring action involved may be painful for the person with arthritic hands. Again, prepacked, dehydrated, or frozen vegetables (which can be bought in bulk for the deep freezer), may help many people, and are certainly useful as a standby.

Casserole meals cut down the number of dishes required, but they may be difficult to lift from the oven when cooked. If this is a difficulty, it may be advisable to turn the oven to its lowest temperature, and wait for another member of the family to lift the dish from the oven.

All serving and washing up activities are made easier with a trolley. For the person in a wheelchair it should be light and free-running, but the housewife who is able to walk will require a strongly made type with high quality castors and a braking mechanism so that it can be used as a walking aid as well.

Tableware should be lightweight and break-resistant, for it will be easier to handle and will stand up to accidental dropping. If plates are stacked on vertical racks which separate the different sizes, it will be easier to select the plates required. Stainless steel cutlery requires less cleaning than silver, but if silver is used it can be kept bright by using a special cloth which needs little pressure to produce a shine, and if the cutlery is kept in polythene bags it will not tarnish easily.

Dishwashers are available in both small and large sizes, including some which can be sited on a table top provided it is near to a water supply and drainage. They are of great benefit to the disabled housewife for they wash, and dry all dishes, pans and cutlery in one operation. Washing up in a bowl or sink is made easier if the dishes are first soaked, as they will then require little pressure from a cloth or dish mop to get them clean. If washed in a detergent and sprayed with clean water from a hose attached to the tap, or a special spring tap, they can then be left to dry naturally.

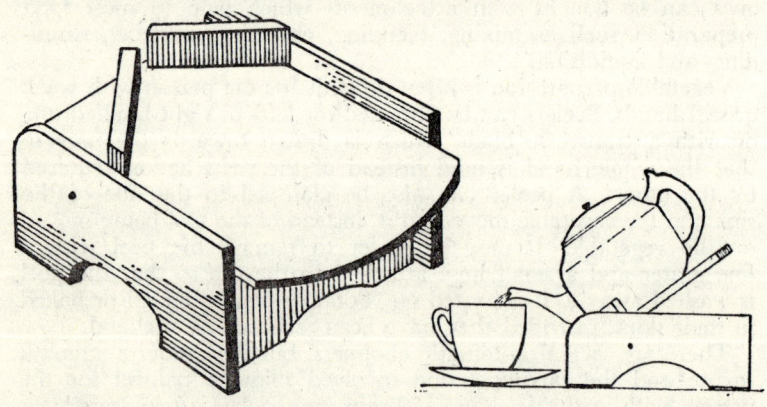

Tilting teapot stand

If it is difficult to fill a kettle by holding it under the tap, a length of hose which will reach from the tap to the cooker can be used and the kettle can stay on the stove ready to be heated. The water should be allowed to run slowly so that there is no likelihood of the kettle filling too quickly, and overflowing.

A tilting teapot stand, which can also be used for a kettle, will tip the teapot to the required angle for pouring so that it is unnesessary to lift it. This aid is available from most occupational therapy departments or the British Red Cross Society.

A rubbish container in the kitchen is also essential and there are many types to choose from. Some can be attached to the inside of a sink unit cupboard, others are free-standing with a pedal attachment for opening the lid, and others have a swing-top opening. The latter type have been found useful for many disabled housewives in a wheelchair for it is not necessary to reach or bend down when using it. All indoor refuse containers are more hygienic and easier to empty if they are lined with plastic bin-liners which can be lifted with their contents from the bin, fastened with a wire tape, and easily transported to the dustbin.

Outside refuse bins are best kept undercover and as near to the kitchen door as practical. Plastic bins are lighter to handle, and the lids are easier to lift. If it is difficult to move them for collection, a specially designed trolley can be used for this purpose.

9

The Disabled Child

THE major problems of the child with a physical disability will arise from the restrictions the disability imposes upon him, and it is in this area that parents must work to ensure that their child is given equal or alternative means to develop independently and intellectually.

Naturally parents tend to be over-protective, for the absence of a limb, a muscular weakness or some other impairment may appear more of a handicap to the onlooker than it is to the person themselves. The body has many compensatory features, the greatest one of which is its ability to adapt to circumstances. The child who is born with the absence of an arm or leg or a deformity of some kind, if given encouragement to seek alternative means of achieving an objective, will use compensatory movements or trick movements. Most people are aware of the remarkable agility of the feet and legs of the children and young people who have been born with no arms, or of how the child who is unable to use his legs will accomplish astonishing manoeuvrability with a wheelchair. In the main these children have been encouraged towards this independence by parents, doctors and therapists, so that they are able to be treated as individuals in their own right.

Each disability affecting children will present its own problems, and the range of impairment within each group is wide. A child may be born with the absence of some fingers, a complete arm, or without any arms. The child born with spina bifida may be severely affected with muscular, bowel and bladder problems, or he may only have a slight handicap such as a limp or slight difficulty with bladder control. Muscular dystrophy may not present any problems in babyhood but from the age of three to five years the child will gradually develop muscular weakness, although here again there are different types with different patterns of weakness. The spastic (cerebral palsy) child may have slight or very severe disability, and his major problems will be dependent upon the amount of brain damage present. These diseases, together with Still's disease (juvenile rheumatoid arthritis), blindness, deafness and congenital heart defect, represent the majority of physically disabling diseases affecting small children.

It is important that the family should continue to function as a unit when caring for a disabled child, for a stable home background is essential for normal development. Obviously, at first, the baby will take a great deal of time and attention until a routine has been established, but once this has been achieved he must play his part as a member of the family. He must get used to more than one person caring for him so that his mother and father can go out or away for short periods without him. This is essential, for all too often a mother devotes too much attention to the disabled child at the expense of caring for her husband and the other children. As far as possible, she should encourage the child to experiment, explore and do things for himself. Often one hears a child say to his mother "*I* can do it" and struggle valiantly to put on a coat which is inside out, or fit shoes on to the wrong feet. The disabled child will also have the natural impulse to behave thus. He may well be physically unable to do some things to help himself, but if he wants to do so he should be allowed to try. He should be encouraged to learn for himself the easiest way of doing things, for it might be a way that no one else would devise. Naturally, he may take a long time to do it, but at least he will have the satisfaction of knowing it was his own effort. Some activities will obviously not be possible, especially for the child with muscular weakness and tiredness. It should then be explained to him that if he is helped to dress, wash and toilet, it will leave him more time to do other things, whether it is school work, a particular hobby, or even helping another member of the family with some less tiring activity.

It is partly because of the natural tendency to protect disabled children and do things for them that mistakes have been made in assessing their mental capabilities, for the physical acts of trying to do things for themselves provide necessary mental stimulation.

Mental stimulation is very important, and the disabled child must initially rely very heavily on the rest of the family for this. He should be included in family discussions, and asked for his opinions and suggestions. It is unwise to talk about him in his presence, whether about his achievements, failures or his health, for children easily get an exaggerated sense of their own importance and become rather spoilt. He should be disciplined in the same way as another child, if it is necessary, for good manners will make him more socially acceptable as he becomes older.

When it is impossible for the child to go out on his own, family outings should be arranged to cover things that he can enjoy. Physically handicapped children are better off today than they have ever been, because more people are aware of their needs and there is less tendency incorrectly to equate physical disability with mental retardation. They should be allowed to mix as much as possible with non-handicapped children for they can learn much from each other. The whole social climate towards disabled people is changing, and more efforts are being made to integrate them into the community. Facilities are becoming increasingly available to give them access to public buildings such as theatres, libraries and civil halls. Wheelchairs which are specially designed for children, including some that are small enough to be taken in a car boot or on public transport, can be provided under the National Health Service. If the child finds it difficult to walk but is reluctant to use a wheelchair, it should be explained to him how much more he will be able to do with the rest of the family if he will use the wheelchair for some outings.

The disabled child should be given every encouragement to receive a normal education, if necessary continuing to higher and university level, for in many cases opportunities in adult life will be greater following the benefit of a good, comprehensive education. Many disabled people have to seek employment which involves intellectual rather than physical ability, therefore they should be given every encouragement, from an early age, to absorb as much education as possible.

Here again, there is a refreshing attitude away from the restricted approach of the early part of the century when every effort was made to segregate the physically handicapped. Under the comprehensive system the physically handicapped child can be fully integrated into normal school life, and only those who are multi-handicapped (mentally as well as physically), or those children who are so physically disabled as to be unable to manage in the slowest stream, need separate schooling. Of course, much will depend upon the architectural problems and the attitude of the school staff, but in general the physically handicapped child will gain much from, and contribute to, the life of an ordinary school.

Through the information available from voluntary societies, such as the Spastic Society, the Muscular Dystrophy Group, the Spina Bifida Association and others, parents can learn much of the disease itself, the problems that arise, and the best way to cope with situations as they develop. These voluntary societies provide an invaluable service, but many parents do not know of their existence and continue to struggle alone. One of the particular advantages of these associations are the group meetings which are held in various parts of the country, where parents can meet and discuss together some of the problems and the means of overcoming them, thus they are able to share experiences, exchange ideas and help each other to come to terms with their problems.

Toilet training

Toilet training can be one of the most difficult aspects of child care and it is not easy to generalize on the best methods of coping with problems. First of all, it is important to establish a regular routine and to make the child use his "pot," and later the lavatory, at a set time each day so that the body will regulate itself for this function at a particular time.

The correct and most comfortable pot which has good stability is very important, and the type with a raised piece in the front will give the child something to hold on to for balance. In the early stages the mother may find it easier to support the child on her lap with the pot held between her knees and the child's back resting against her body. When he is able to sit upright alone the pot should be placed in a stable position, preferably in a corner or against a wall so that the child can feel reasonably secure.

As the child grows, a child-size toilet seat can be used over a normal lavatory pan, and some children may need the additional support of grab rails at a convenient height around the toilet. So that the child can learn to be as independent as possible, the flush handle should be sited where he can reach it, and not require too much pressure. Soft tissue toilet paper is comfortable and easy to use and also ensures that he is as dry and clean as possible, thus preventing any soreness.

If the child is still in napkins when he is four years old it may be necessary to adopt stricter measures. If he is able to communicate his needs, then a spell without nappies when he becomes wet and uncomfortable will make it easier to explain, and for him to understand, how necessary it is for this function to be performed in the lavatory.

The child who is born without his upper limbs will experience special difficulties in becoming independent for toilet purposes. In many instances such a child is able to use his feet instead of his hands, but he obviously needs a great deal of training. When he is old enough to use standard lavatories it may be necessary to use one or two steps so that he can reach the toilet easily. Cleaning the perineum can often be achieved by "sitting on the heel," a technique which involves placing a pad of toilet paper on the heel on which the child then squats to clean himself. Other such children use a toilet stick with the toilet paper clipped to one end. Some prefer to put paper on to something solid and of a convenient shape so that they can sit on the paper. A specially designed toilet stick will enable the small boy to unzip his trousers and use the toilet independently.

Clothing generally has to be adapted for toilet purposes, with front or flap opening fasteners. An ordinary zip with a larger size ring on it is often easily managed, or a Velcro fastening can be used to replace a zip. Girls' pants can be adapted by sewing loops to the waistband so that they can use their feet, teeth, or a dressing stick for pulling them up and down.

Incontinence is a particular problem because of the social disadvantages as well as the domestic ones. Advice can be obtained from the local hospital paediatric department, for there are many methods now both in terms of aids and appliances (particularly for boys) and surgical procedures (particularly for girls) which can overcome some of the major problems of urinary incontinence.

Bowel incontinence must be managed by the development of a routine of evacuation which can be taught by the hospital staff.

Bathing

It is very important that the child should be made to feel as safe as possible, therefore bathing should be a leisurely procedure when the parents have time to talk to him and show him how to play with bath toys, sponges and water. When the child begins to sit up and crawl, the bath should be equipped with a non-slip mat and possibly some form of bath seat. Sometimes parents are able to adapt and design the most suitable bath seat for their

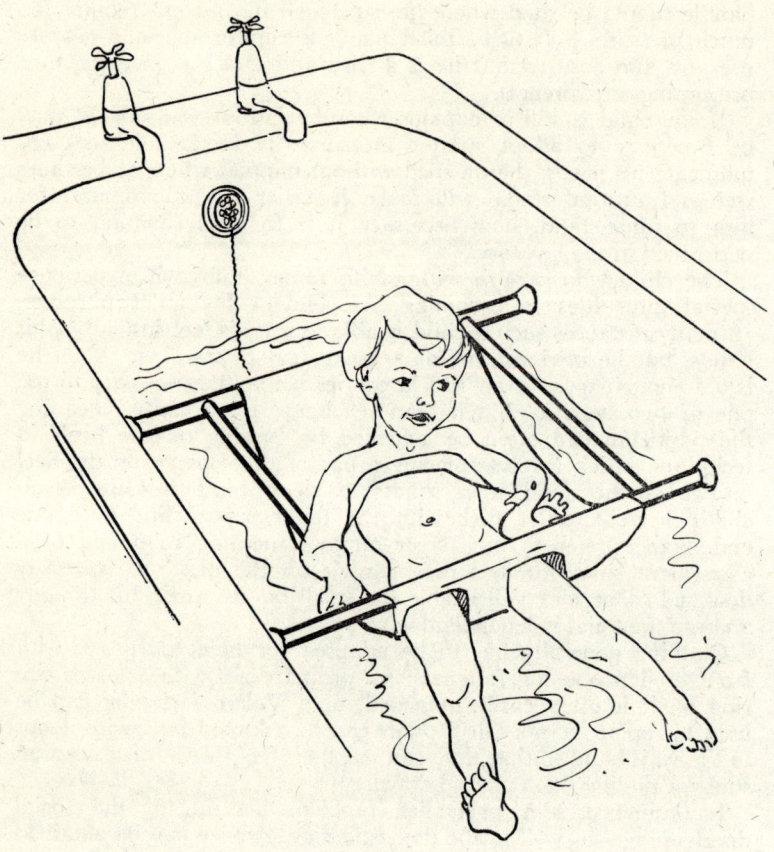

Bath frame holds young child safely, leaving mother's hands free to wash the child and also allows the child to kick and splash safely

child's requirements, and there are many on the commercial market. The Spastic Society can supply a "Safabath" seat which has been used successfully by many parents.

It is advisable not to use too much water, and to drain the water out before lifting the child from the bath. This will enable his mother to wrap him in a large towel so that he is easier to manage.

As he grows, he should be given every encouragement to do as much as possible for himself, and grab rails should be installed in the bathroom so that he will have plenty of support. Many of the suggestions in Chapter 4 on Personal Appearance will prove helpful for the growing child.

Clothing and dressing

The small baby will be most comfortably and suitably dressed in an all-in-one terry towelling garment, which will make it easier to pick him up, dress and undress him. Nylon garments tend to be rather slippery, and may therefore make it more difficult to handle the baby. All clothing should have adequate neck and arm openings for ease of dressing, and dungarees and trousers will be easier to manage if they are fastened down the centre seam of the leg. Velcro can be used to enlarge or replace existing openings and make it easier for the child to dress himself as he grows more independent. Slip on shoes will be less trouble than shoes with straps or laces. As soon as he is old enough he should be given every encouragement to dress himself, and aids such as dressing sticks should be provided if necessary. If he experiences difficulty in standing then he should put on as many clothes as possible while sitting down, and use the wall for support when standing.

Children with muscular weakness or imbalance may develop severe deformities, particularly of the legs, which seriously interfere with dressing. In these circumstances it is worth discussing with the paediatrician the possibility of corrective surgery for the deformities, even if such a procedure will not contribute to the child's ability to walk. Apart from improving ease of dressing, such an operation also improves the appearance of the feet and legs, and this may be of importance to the child himself.

Eating and drinking (see also Chapter 6)

Most children manage to make a mess when they are learning to feed themselves, therefore one of the first needs is for adequate protection, both for the person and the table. A coverall plastic bib or apron is very useful, together with a plastic traycloth for table or high-chair tray. The plates which are sold in baby departments of most large stores and chemists shops are particularly suitable for the needs of a child with weakened or impaired grip, for they allow the food to be pushed to the edge of the plate thus making it easier to lift on to the spoon or fork. The Manoy range of tableware was specially designed for the needs of disabled people. The plate has a built up edge and the spoon and fork are angled for easy handling. The cup is designed as a goblet without a protruding handle, but with a cut-out stem which enables it to be held in many different ways depending on the disability. This range of tableware is available from large stores dealing in the Melaware range of goods, and has been found especially useful for some disabled children.

If it is not possible to use ordinary cutlery then special, or adapted cutlery may be necessary. Handles may be made thicker with a piece of plastic foam taped on with Velcro, or made longer by attaching a piece of balsa wood or rigid plastic strip to the existing handle and binding with sticky tape, but all these adaptations make cleanliness and hygiene difficult to achieve. More permanent adaptations to the handles can be made in occupational therapy departments or by an ingenious handyman.

If plates have a tendency to slip Copydex painted on the underside of the plate, or a thin plastic foam sheet used as a table mat, will reduce this problem. If it cannot be solved in this way then it may be possible to make a tray or small table from plywood with cut-out holes to hold the plate, dish or cup.

One of the most widely used aids is the Flexi-straw which is a curved drinking straw. Also useful are straws made from plastic tubing, such as those used by racing cyclists, and which enable a drink to be placed on a table or wheelchair tray at a convenient height, thus dispensing with the need to hold a cup or tip it for drinking. If necessary, they can be clipped to the cup by using a fountain pen holder, which can be obtained from any stationers. The straws are available from most chemists shops and the plastic tubing from cycle shops.

A mug with two handles may also be helpful in the early stages of teaching a child to drink by himself, for it is easier to hold and he will feel more confident. It is wise to start with small quantities of liquid at first. A two handled beaker can be obtained from the Spastics Society, and there are several designs of non-spillable cups and mugs for children, some of which are fitted with lids and/or drinking spouts.

Presentation of food is extremely important, and care should be taken to make it appear appetising and colourful as well as nutritious. If cutting up food is a problem, meat should be minced or given in small pieces, such as stews or casseroles, and vegetables should be diced or mashed. It is a mistake to keep a child on baby food for too long and he should be encouraged to start solid foods, which need a certain amount of chewing, as soon as possible. Diet is extremely important, for the disabled child who is allowed to become overweight will present many problems. Starchy and sweet foods should be avoided as much as possible, and a well balanced diet containing plenty of fresh fruit and vegetables should be given. There is often a natural tendency for parents and relatives to spoil a disabled child and allow him to over indulge in sweets and sweet foods. This tendency must be resisted because it is not good for the child, and if he becomes overweight it adds considerably to the difficulties of lifting and transporting him.

Mobility

In the early stages of childhood, a normal type of pram is

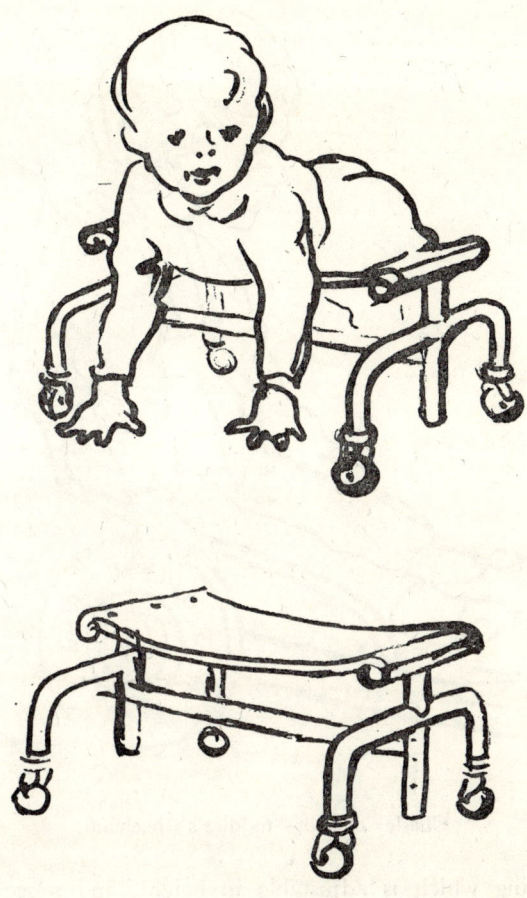

Infant crawler

generally quite suitable, although the mother of a spastic child
may need special advice on the most comfortable and suitable
form of transport. As the child grows, suitable aids will have to be
provided for the child who has weakness of the trunk and leg
muscles, or generalized weakness.

An infant crawler, on which the child can support his body
whilst using his hands and feet to move along is very useful for the
child with weak back muscles, and it will help him in learning to
crawl. The infant crawler is constructed of steel tubing and a

93

Chailey chariot—toddler's wheelchair

vynide sling which is adjustable in height, and moves on easy running castors.

Another wheeled device for the very young child is the Chailey Chariot. This is a brightly painted little trolley on three wheels which is manoeuvrable but very stable, and can be propelled by a baby from nine to twelve months of age, thus enabling him to play with toys on the floor. This device can be supplied through the National Health Service as it is regarded as a child's wheel-chair.

Another very popular device for young children is the "Lobster Pot" walking aid. This is a frame constructed of aluminium alloy which moves on four small castors. The upper body ring is padded with sponge rubber which supports a soft hammock type sling with cut-out holes for the child's legs. The child is then supported by a shoulder harness with his feet just touching the floor, and is able to move around without further support. Many children gain enormous pleasure from this device. Again, it is available through the hospital service, but advice from a consultant will usually have to be obtained before it can be provided.

Lightweight walking frames with brightly coloured wheels, and handgrips, or with adjustable legs are also available for children. Some incorporate a seat and a forearm support.

For the more severely disabled child, wheeled transport can take the form of a large pram which is specially designed for children who need to be in a reclining or semi-reclining position. Alternatively, small portable wheelchairs, such as the Baby Buggy or Buggy Major which are small and very light to handle, and which can be folded and carried with one hand for taking on public transport, are particularly useful.

Many standard types of self-propelled wheelchairs are available, and the Yorkhill (Model 3Y) specially for children from two to six years, was designed at a hospital. This chair is lightweight and compact, can be self-propelled or attendant propelled and partially folded for storage, but it is designed for indoor use only.

Many other wheelchairs are provided in child and adult sizes, with adjustments to armrests, footrests, trays and headrests, and if the disability is particularly severe, a powered wheelchair can be provided. These chairs are powered by a battery motor and electrically operated, and give a great number of children an independence which they could not otherwise achieve.

A tricycle is also available under the National Health Service for the disabled child as a means of outdoor mobility. These tricycles have adjustable seats and handlebars. By selecting the correct adaptation many children with weakness, deformity or inco-ordination can achieve considerable independence of mobility.

Many of these aids for mobility are available under the National Health Service from the Artificial Limb and Appliance Centres, and enquiries should be made through a general practitioner or hospital doctor. General practitioners can only prescribe from a limited range of standard wheelchairs, and the selection and prescription of more specialized wheelchairs and aids require referral to a hospital. Often there are facilities for attendance at a Wheelchair Clinic, either at a hospital, rehabilitation centre or at an Artificial Limb and Appliance Centre, where specialist advice is available, and, most importantly, where there is an opportunity for different wheelchairs to be tried out so that a correct selection can be made.

Play

The ability to play is a vital part of a child's development and learning, and not just a way of passing the time. First social contacts are made through playing, for by sharing interests communication and friendships develop.

The disabled child who is prevented by his handicap from joining in many strenuous games should be encouraged to develop play activities within the range of his ability. It is important that he should be given toys for which he can develop an affection, such as cuddly toys, and by carefully watching his development parents will learn which objects give more pleasure than others. It is a mistake to assume that all little girls love dolls and all little boys love motor cars.

More and more toys are being devised which are particularly suitable for children of all ages, sizes and needs. It is now generally recognized that play is an important therapy for a child in hospital, and studies have taken place on the psychological reaction of children who need to stay in hospital for prolonged periods of time. Many hospitals now appoint play leaders who are specially trained to watch over long stay children and teach them to develop their interests and needs. Playing with sand, plasticine, and paint are all encouraged, for it is known that many children find this an emotional outlet.

It is not usually necessary to have specially adapted toys for physically handicapped children, for many of them will select their own choice from the toys and games which give them particular pleasure, but certain toys will also have a therapeutic value in exercising muscles which would not otherwise have the chance of movement.

Baby dolls : The child can develop an affection for this toy and in playing with it, dressing and undressing, achieve mobility of the shoulders, wrists and hands.

Teddy bears : Always a favourite with children ranging in age from nine months to eighteen years. Most children love small furry animals, and this can act as a substitute. Playing with it can also exercise the hands and arms of the small child.

Hammer toys : Very popular game for most children with a physical disability, particularly those wearing an artificial arm, for the two handed activity will ensure that they use both hands. Also good for co-ordination.

Puzzles : Many of these are now available with extra large pieces which are particularly useful for the child with an artificial arm or weak hand control.

Good intellectual exercise.

Building and construction kits : Any type of construction game from simple cylinders or boxes of bricks, to more sophisticated interlocking bricks which make model buildings such as Lego, are good for all ages. They provide good exercise and hand control together with the need to use imagination.

Modelling clay, sand, painting, crayoning : All of these are good for they provide a natural creative outlet. Painting need not necessarily be done with a brush held in the hand, if the hands are weak it can be held in the mouth or in the toes. However, brushes are not always necessary, finger paints are very popular. The important thing in painting is to encourage self-expression.

Counting frames : Particularly useful for the three to four years old; will develop mental control and finger dexterity.

Needlework : Weaving, embroidery, sewing picture cards, knitting, either from a knitting dolly or needles, will prove an interesting and useful hobby.

Hand puppets : The older child will experience enormous pleasure from hand puppets, many of which they can devise for themselves. They can be encouraged to perform little playlets for entertainment of their family and friends.

Miniature cars : Useful as collectors items, and small enough to be played with on a table or wheelchair tray.

Squeezy toys : Loved by most babies, particularly if they make a noise. Larger ones particularly useful and pleasing for the spastic child as they encourage grip.

Toy drums : Useful for letting off steam. Most children love musical instruments and this can prove a useful means of developing a sense of rythym.

Xylophone : The size of this instrument, together with the small amount of effort needed to play it will be very suitable for some children.

Dominoes and draughts : Now available in extra large sizes so that they are easy to handle.

Chinese chequers, ludo, draughts, chess, monopoly : Suitable for the older child and particularly good for developing social behaviour and patience.

Soap bubbles : A great favourite with children of all ages. Good basis for speech training.

Ball games : Graduated ball sizes will allow most children to play games, larger balls being easier to catch for the child in a wheelchair. Good exercise for balance and co-ordination. Particularly good for spastic children.

Tricycle, go-carts : Many of these can be adapted suitably for physically handicapped children by retaining straps for the body and feet, lengthened handles, or a control stick for attendant. Occupational therapists can advise on adaptations.

Typewriters : Not necessarily a toy but a very useful means of expression for the spastic child or the child with weak hands who can be taught to use a mouth stick for hitting the keys. Special rolls of paper can be purchased which avoid the need to replace the paper frequently.

Kites: Many children in wheelchairs can enjoy the pleasure of flying a kite when taken for a trip in the country by car.

Dressing up: All children love to take part in playlets or charades, and the child in a wheelchair can become all sorts of things by adding a shawl or a hat.

Further advice on play and toys can often be obtained through the paediatric departments of the hospital service. The British Toy Council, and Toy Libraries Association (addresses in Sources of Information, p. 182–85 are also helpful on this matter.

CASE HISTORY

David has muscular dystrophy and spends most of his time in a wheelchair. He lives with his parents and younger sister in a small market town and goes to the local school, which is only a short distance from his home.

David sleeps downstairs and with the help of a grant from the local authority his father has built on a bathroom and toilet next to his bedroom. This has made the daily routine very much easier for David's mother who helps him to get up and wash and dress in time for school. His parents have always encouraged him to be as independent as possible and in the evening when there is plenty of time, David can manage to get himself ready for bed, transferring sideways from his wheelchair with the aid of a sliding board.

His father and uncle laid a large area of paving at the back of the house and made a ramp from the door so that David can wheel himself into the garden.

As it is not easy for him to go to friends' houses to play, his mother has always made a point of welcoming other children. But it is hard for a small boy who is unable to join in all the fun with other children, and it was especially hard when his sister and two of her friends joined the junior branch of the County Naturalists' Trust and went off on exciting field outings. David became discouraged and apathetic, and his father realized that he must find something that his son could do equally well, if not better, than his friends. The father of one of the other children helped to provide the answer. He came and sat with David in the garden and taught him to recognize and watch all the garden birds. Then he made nesting boxes and asked David to help him with a serious study of bluetits. He was to watch and record the dates when the birds first inspected the boxes, how they prepared them, when they started to take nesting material into the box and so on; and then how many times in an hour the birds carried food to the nestlings.

David was enthralled with his new hobby and when his observations began to be recorded in the local Naturalist Trust's magazine, he became the "bird expert" among the children in the neighbourhood.

10

The Disabled Mother

WHEN a mother is disabled, much will depend upon whether her disability is longstanding and she has come to terms with her handicap and limitations. If, however, she became disabled after marriage it may be much more difficult for her to cope with husband and children at the same time that she is trying to live with her new disability. Sometimes a mother becomes handicapped after she has had a child and she may take the decision to have another. Physical disability does not necessarily mean that a young woman is unable to become a mother, but taking care of a child may well be fraught with problems. Experience has shown that it is possible to look after a baby and young children, even if she is quite severely handicapped.

There is an increasing tendency for severely disabled people to marry and to want to have children. Firstly, it is wise to discuss the general implications, particularly to understand the chances of the disability being hereditary. There are now specialist advisory services available in several parts of the country who can assess this in a scientific fashion. This advice can be obtained through the hospital service, or sometimes through the help of specialist charitable organizations concerned with specific disabilities. (See Sources of Information, p. 182.)

Another trend is for two disabled people to want to marry. Not only may this have genetic implications but it may also have important repercussions in the general organization of home life. If the father is too disabled to work he may be able to help considerably in the home, and the planning of aids and activities must be done around the combined activities.

The young disabled girl who is contemplating marriage will, inevitably, wonder whether she should become a mother, and whether it will be possible for her to cope with a very small baby. She should seek advice from her doctor who will be able to tell her whether it is advisable, from the physical point of view, for her to have a family, but no one can tell her exactly how she will manage, for she and her husband will devise and develop different methods of management as they reach each stage of the child's life. For the disabled mother it is more than usually advisable to plan ahead before the baby arrives, and to decide which activities of babycare can safely be done by the mother and which by some-one else.

It is usual nowadays for health visitors to follow up at home after the birth of all babies, and whether the baby was delivered in hospital or at home, the young disabled mother will have the full support of district nurses, health visitors, and other members of the social services.

Bathing a very young baby is a problem which worries most inexperienced mothers, for the prospect of holding a tiny, wet and slippery human being can be very daunting. Training is given in most maternity hospitals before the mother leaves their care, and at home the district nurse will be able to advise, for naturally the mother will want to learn as quickly as possible to look after her baby herself. First of all it is important to decide at what level the bath or bowl is to be placed. Some people find it easier to put it on a low table, others prefer to put it on the floor and kneel to bath the baby, laying him on a towel on the floor to dry thus saving some of the lifting problems. Sometimes a kitchen sink is used because the hot and cold water is easily available, and it is easy to drain the water away, but the taps may be an obstruction unless mixer taps are used, for these can be pushed to one side when not in use.

Undressing and potting the baby may take quite a long time, therefore it is advisable to have two jugs of water available, one containing hot water and the other cold, so that the correct temperature can be obtained when it is required. If the bath is filled before the baby is undressed then it may be too cool before it is needed. It is not necessary to use a great deal of water.

An alternative to bathing the baby in the bath, is to wash him all over while he is lying on a bed or table which has been covered with a waterproof sheet and a towel. This may prove a more practical alternative if the mother is unsure of herself.

If bathing is delayed until the father comes home in the even-

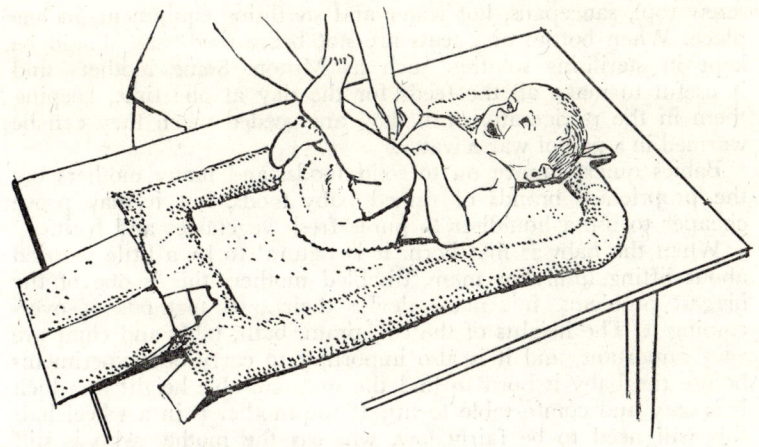

Top 'n Tail mattress for nappy changing. The raised edge helps to prevent baby rolling off. The end pocket holds talc etc.

ing this will often prove safer, and will also let him have some of the fun of caring for the baby.

A trolley which can hold a pail for napkins, powder, creams, soap and sponge, together with the baby's clean clothes, is an essential piece of equipment. It is easy to pull forward when needed and pushed out of the way when no longer required.

If it is too difficult to hold the baby on the lap when dressing him, a table covered with a soft blanket, or a special mattress with raised sides, such as the "Top 'n' Tail" mattress (available from large stores selling baby items) will hold the baby safely while he is being dressed.

Easy-to-manage clothing should be purchased. Disposable napkins will save laundry, but some babies are intolerant of them. If pins are too difficult to manage for fastening the napkins then they can be fastened with small strips of Velcro (always remembering to close the Velcro with a spare strip when laundering). Vests with envelope type neck openings are easy to slip on and off, and an all in one terry towelling suit or sleeping bag will cover the baby warmly and sensibly and make it unnecessary to worry about small garments like bootees, socks and jackets. Waterproof pants that fasten at the sides with snap fasteners will be easier to put on than the type that need to be pulled on, and garments that fasten at the front will also be easier to manage.

If the baby is bottle-fed, it is advisable to have all the necessary items such as milk-feed, bottles, teats (which are available with a screw top), saucepans, hot water and sterilising equipment, in one place. When bottles and teats are not being used they should be kept in sterilising solution such as Milton. Some mothers find it useful to make all the feeds for the day at one time, keeping them in the refrigerator until they are needed when they can be warmed in a pan of warm water.

Babies quickly move on to solid foods, and many mothers use the proprietary brands of tinned baby foods, but it may prove cheaper to use a liquidiser to purée fresh vegetables and fruit.

When the baby is first born, it is natural to be a little worried about lifting him. For many disabled mothers this is one of the biggest problems, but many devise their own methods of overcoming it. The heights of the cot, pram, bath, table and chair are very important, and it is also important to carry out experiments before the baby is born to find the most suitable height at which it is easy and comfortable to lift. If the mother is in a wheelchair this will need to be fairly low, whereas the mother who is stiff and unable to bend a great deal, will need all the equipment fairly high.

It is sometimes helpful if the baby is laid on a draw sheet which the mother can pull towards her and lift by placing the two sides of the sheet together, thus making a hammock to lift the baby. From about the age of six to nine months the child will be able to sit up on his own and he will be able to push his feet and hold out his arms which will help the lifting process.

For the more severely disabled it is possible to use mechanical devices such as hoists, but this needs skilled assessment and advice from an occupational therapist or physiotherapist with experience in this type of work.

Once the child is able to walk he will naturally take a few tumbles and the mother may be worried about how she will be able to pick him up. As a rule, many with this problem find that the child will pick himself up, knowing instinctively that he has to do so, and will then run to his mother for the necessary sympathy and comfort.

The choice of prams and carrycots is wide, but the dual purpose pram/carrycot is particularly suitable for the disabled mother, for it is small enough to wheel around the house and can be detached from the wheels to take upstairs or out in a car.

When the child grows too big for a carrycot a dropside cot will be necessary. It is sometimes helpful if the rail at one side of the cot is cut through at the centre and the sides hinged so that it opens like a gate and fastens with a suitable locking device, thus making it easier to lift the child in and out of the cot.

Many highchairs are too difficult for a disabled mother to lift her child into, and she should look for a type which is adjustable in height and very stable. Models are available which allow the

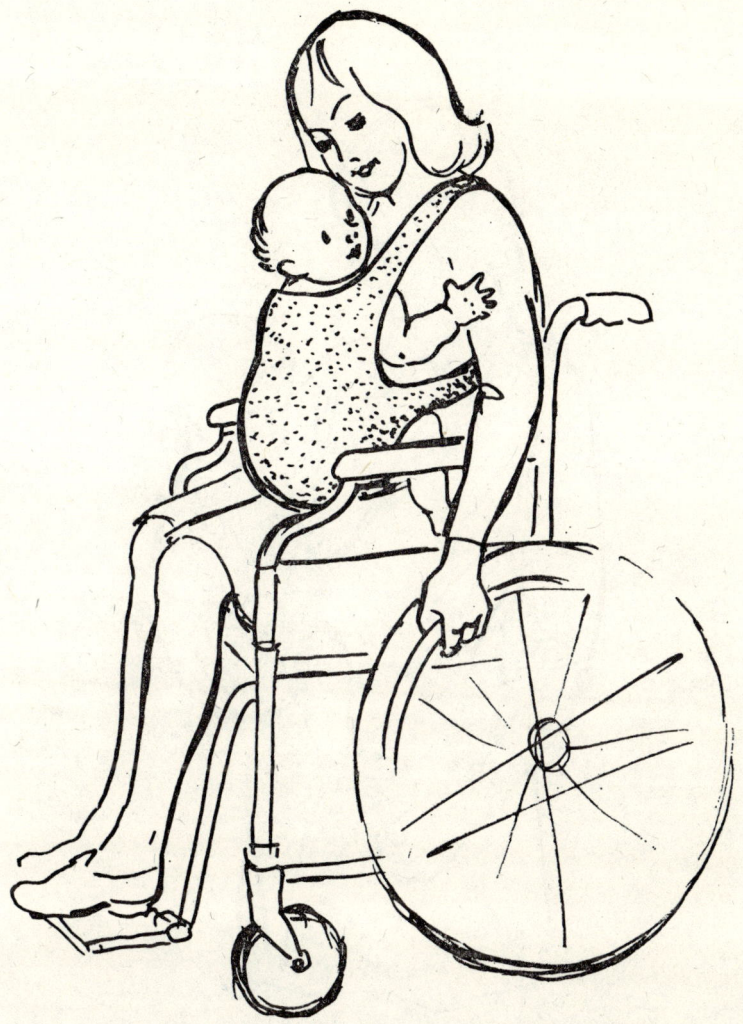

Baby sling leaving mother's hands free to propel wheelchair

baby to sit and lie, or adapt to a "potty" chair, a high chair, low chair, and even a swing. They also fold sufficiently to be carried easily.

Playpens are also difficult for the disabled mother to manage. The size, and the fact that they are usually at floor level and need to be folded and unfolded for use, make them very cumbersome.

Baby sling for hemiplegic mother

If a large room is available then it may be possible to use the type with a built in floor, and adjust the legs to a convenient height. The sides can also be altered as suggested for a dropside cot. In practice however, small children soon become very agile and quickly find a way out of the playpen. So, in the long run, it may prove simpler to allow the child to crawl about in a room that has been made free from hazards, such as power sockets (which he may push his fingers into), tablecloths which he can pull off the table, trailing electric wires, and of course, fires which should always be surrounded by a fire guard. As an added precaution against the child's exploratory nature, it may be advisable to tie the handles of cupboard doors so that they cannot be opened easily.

One need not necessarily be disabled to wonder how one is going to cope with the varying stages of development in a child, and physical limitation does not prevent a woman from becoming a good mother. In many respects there are advantages, for the child soon learns how he must help himself instead of expecting his mother to do things for him. He also develops a greater sense of security because his mother is nearly always there when he needs her.

The physically handicapped mother will often not be able to run about after the child, and she must therefore from the very beginning build a basic trust with him. He must learn from the tone of her voice when she is playing and when she is being serious. Discipline is important for a child's development and it can be achieved without harshness but by a kind, yet firm, manner. The mother would be well advised to learn what she should look for at each stage of a child's development, so that she is able to understand his limitations and when he can be encouraged to do things for himself.

Some mothers with a handicap feel that they are at a disadvantage because they are unable to play with their children. As a rule, children prefer their parents to enjoy their quieter pastimes, such as story telling, drawing, painting, jigsaw puzzles and so on, preferring to play their more boisterous games with other children.

Playgroups for pre-school age children are particularly valuable for an only child, for he can learn to mix socially with other children. If it is not possible for either of the parents to take the child to such a group, then a local social worker may be able to find someone, possibly another mother, who could take the child for her.

As the child grows older and is more able to manage for himself about the house, the major problem for the more severely disabled mother is one of transport—to school, shops and social activities. Cars are not generally available through the National Health

Service, but they can be provided as an alternative to the standard three-wheeler or a private car allowance if : "an eligible disabled parent, who is able to drive and is, for a substantial part of the day in sole charge of his, or her, young child."

Such a car can be converted to hand controls if required, and is insured by the Department of Health and Social Security and exempt from vehicle excise duty. They are replaced free of charge when necessary, unless the replacement has to be provided because of negligence. All maintenance and repairs are the responsibility of the disabled person, but an allowance is paid towards this expense. Further enquiries about this facility should be made to the local office of the Department of Health and Social Security.

CASE HISTORY

Carol and Colin both became disabled in childhood, and learned when quite young to make the most of their plus factors, and accept the remaining limitations. Colin is permanently in a wheelchair but has fairly strong arms, and Carol who has had juvenile rheumatoid arthritis (Still's disease) has hips and knees which are stiff, but pain free. She is able to get around their bungalow using one crutch or a trolley as a walking aid. Her elbows and shoulders have very limited movement and her wrists and hands are weak and painful.

They have now been married for a number of years and have two children. Initially there were big problems, caused by Carol's painful wrists which made orthodox methods of lifting and carrying impossible. Colin therefore lifted the baby whenever necessary and placed him into a carrycot on wheels so that Carol was able to push him around the house. She changed nappies while the baby was in his pram, and bathed him in the sink. Colin put the baby on to the floor to play, and although Carol could not reach the floor at all, the baby helped himself by clinging to both of them to an unusual degree so that by teamwork they were able to lift him.

The babies slept in a separate room from a very early age, because it was felt that the noise of the wheelchairs and the transferring into bed would be too disturbing. They were dressed in all-in-one sleeping suits so that if they did manage to kick the bedclothes off, they were still adequately covered, but for good measure the blankets were safety-pinned into place.

Four years after the birth of their first child they had another little boy. By this time the elder child was able to be quite helpful, and was able to do quite a lot of the fetching and carrying necessary for the new baby and felt quite important looking after his brother. He had by now learned that if he fell over he must pick himself up and go to his mother for comfort, and that he must obey without hesitation when asked to do something. Unfortunately the second child did not acquire this habit quite so readily, but through a firm, quiet manner Carol and Colin are gradually making him understand.

The telephone is an essential piece of equipment in their home, and they have taught the children to answer it, and to use it to call for help if necessary. On one occasion Carol fell in the garden and was unable to help herself, but the eldest child followed his mother's instructions and was able to telephone for the doctor, and to get a cushion to make his mother more comfortable while they waited for help to come.

The children are constantly learning new methods of self-reliance and how to help their parents. They are always encouraged to have their friends in to play, and Carol makes time to join in as many of their activities as she can manage, always being ready to read to them, or sit with them to watch a television programme, listen to their adventures and encourage them with hobbies.

11

Communication

THE ability to read, write and to converse are such natural functions that they are taken as a matter of course. When disability makes it difficult to hold a book, pen or telephone, such as in severe arthritis, or when acute back and neck pain prevent one from bending the head to read, the inability to use these means of communication becomes a severe handicap and alternative methods have to be found.

Many devices and techniques, ranging from simple aids to sophisticated electronic equipment, can be used to overcome some of these problems.

Reading aids

If difficulty is experienced in holding a book because of pain

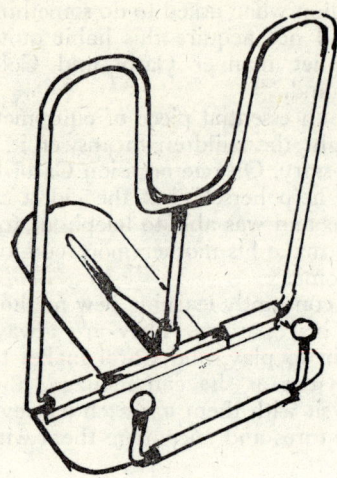

Light bookrest

or deformity in the hands, then a bookrest or a bookstand may be necessary. There are many types of bookstand available, varying in adjustability of height and angle. The position in which it is most easy to read, together with the height of the chair, wheelchair or bed that is used must all be considered when buying. Simple bookrests can be obtained from office suppliers or stationers, and the British Red Cross Society.

Newspapers are often difficult to read in comfort if the arms and shoulders are weak. Daily papers are too large to be placed on a bookstand, and one of the most useful methods yet devised is a light aluminium frame, shaped like a clothes line on wheels, which can be pushed near to a chair or wheelchair. The newspaper is pegged to this with bulldog clips or clothes pegs, and although someone else has to turn the pages for re-pegging, it has been found very useful by people who are unable to read a newspaper in any other way.

Page turners

Turning the page of a book may be difficult for those with weakness or tremor. A rubber thimble such as those used in offices for collating sheets of paper, or by a bank cashier lifts the corner of the page so that it is easy to turn it over.

If the hands and arms are too weak to move then a head-controlled stick which is attached to a band fastened round the head can be used. The book should be placed on a bookrest at approximately eye level when seated, and the head is moved

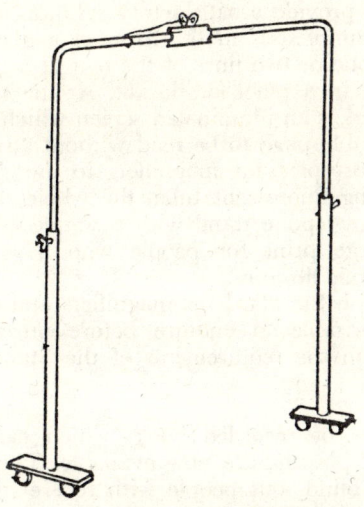

Newspaper holder

forward so that the rubber attachment on the end of the reading stick will turn the page. Both of these methods are more effective if the bookrest has a non-slip surface, such as a thin plastic foam mat.

There are several types of electrically-operated page turners, the reader operating the electric motor for page-turning by means of a micro-switch operated by whatever movement is available, e.g. finger or mouth. One of the cheaper models requires considerable preparation by a helper as a clip must be attached to each page. Another model has a bar with a rubber ferrule to push the pages over one at a time. Electric page turners vary considerably in their efficiency, and only one or two are designed to turn the pages back if needed for reference.

Microfilms

A different solution to the problem is the use of a microfilm projector. There is a library of filmed books, and microfilm projectors can be hired. This service is particularly useful for students who can have text-books microfilmed. This system enables the reader to select passages and to re-read passages, which is essential when studying.

Magnifiers

Physical disability may also be accompanied by poor sight. If spectacles do not provide a satisfactory solution, a magnifier may be helpful. The simplest is in the form of a glass or plastic bar which magnifies one or two lines of the text at a time. Being small it can be carried in a purse or pocket. At the other end of the range of magnifiers is an illuminated screen which supports a book and enables a double page to be read without adjustment.

One of the most pleasant magnifiers to use is a circular one with a surrounding fluorescent tube, the whole device being supported upon an anglepoise stand with a simple adjustment.

Books with large print for people who have poor sight are available from public libraries.

There is a British Standard for magnifiers and bookrests, and if possible it is advisable to enquire before purchasing that the product meets with the requirements of the Standard.

Recorded books

Several libraries of recorded books which can be played on record or cassette players, are now available. These are primarily intended for the blind, but people with severe physical disability may also find them helpful and entertaining.

Tables

Tables supported on the cantilever principle are usually easier to manoeuvre by handicapped people for a comfortable working position over bed or chair. Such tables need to be strongly made, with a range of adjustments which allow them to be set low enough for writing and high enough to hold a book so that the head does not need to be held at an uncomfortable angle for reading. The height and spread of the base should be measured so that it will go under or between the footrests of a wheelchair, easy chair or divan bed. It is also useful if the table is equipped with a ledge deep enough to support a book. If the top of the table is designed to tilt, the locking mechanism should be positive in action and yet easy to operate. Some of the knobs or levers used to fix the adjustment are easier to handle than others, and this should be tried before purchasing.

Writing

Difficulty in writing may derive from an inability to hold a pen or pencil, or to steady the paper, or the difficulty may stem from damage to the thought processes which initiate and control setting down letters and words.

If one hand only is affected it may be easier to learn to write with the other hand, rather than learn to use aids and appliances. It has been found that pencils are easier to control than pens, although felt-tip pens with a fine point may not prove too difficult.

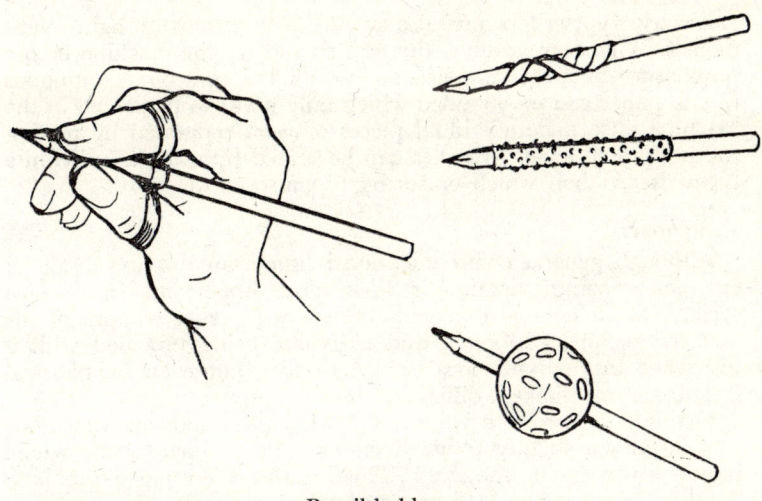

Pencil holders

Among the aids which can be used to help people to write are: pimpled rubber glued around the pen or pencil; a rubber band twisted round the pen or pencil; a plastic practice golf ball through which the pencil is pushed making a large surface to grip; a broad elastic band knotted round the pencil leaving two loops for the thumb and index finger.

Paper can be held in a clip-board if the hand can manoeuvre the clip or someone else can prepare it for use. Magnetic boards are also useful and are available commercially, but it is possible to make one by using a sheet of steel about ten inches by eight inches and two small magnets, which are placed over the corners of the sheet of paper to hold it in place.

For partially sighted writers, a simple guide line can be used, consisting of two slats of cardboard mounted on canvas which can be folded back one at a time as each line is completed.

Typewriters

It is particularly important not to become over-tired when practising writing, or to strive too hard for a high standard. Many people who cannot manipulate a pen or pencil can use a typewriter successfully. Whether it is best to use a machine which is portable or the heavier office type will depend on whether it can be left in its working position, and if not, whether the user can move it himself. The person with spasticity or inco-ordination may need a heavy machine, especially if he is using his toes to type, as he will tend to push the machine away as he types.

Electric typewriters are also available as heavy or lightweight models. Whenever possible, the user should try the machine before purchasing to make sure he can use all the controls. Continuous typing paper can be obtained which only needs to be placed in the machine once and individual pieces of work separated by tearing the perforated edge. Mistakes can be erased by using a half-white typewriter ribbon which erases by typing over the error.

Telephones

Although general communication is important for the disabled, emergency communication is even more important. In modern society, the telephone is a very necessary piece of equipment for disabled people, and more and more are being provided with a telephone through the local social services, but even so, physical disabilities may make it difficult to use.

Dialling is a problem when the fingers and hands are weak, but a stick with a slightly rounded end can be grasped by the whole hand, thus reducing the strain. Holding the receiver while making a call is also tiring. A wall mounted telephone may overcome some of the difficulty, and when making a call the receiver could be clipped to the wall by spring clips thus leaving the hands free.

Post Office telephones now have a wide range of appliances to assist people who experience difficulty in using a telephone and advice can be obtained from the local telephone manager. Amongst these devices the Loudspeaking Telephone is probably one of the most useful. It is possible to receive and make calls using only the loudspeaker and microphone operated by a simple switch. The bell rings for an incoming call as in an ordinary telephone and the call is received by pressing a switch. The telephone has three units which contain the loudspeaker, an amplifier which boosts incoming speech to the loudspeaker, and a control unit which contains the microphone, the dial, the volume control for the loudspeaker, the on/off switch, and a pilot light to indicate that the telephone is switched on. Calls can be made either by using the handset in the usual way or by pressing down a switch and dialling either the number, or the operator. The microphone unit and the loudspeaker should be about three feet apart, and the user should be about eighteen inches from the microphone and speaking towards it. When the call ends the set should be switched off. If dialling is impossible, a "Sender 1" may be added. This is a box, six inches by four by three, with a large knob on the top which when pressed, dials the Post Office telephone operator who will give assistance and obtain the call. Unfortunately, this means that all calls are charged at the operator obtained rate which is considerably higher than the Subscriber Trunk Dialling rate.

Other aids from the Post Office include an extra ear-piece so that the incoming call can be heard with both ears, or with the microphone of the hearing aid. An amplifying head set is also available to increase the volume of the sound, and is controlled by a thumb-wheel in the side of the earpiece. There is also a faint-speech amplifier for the person with a permanently weak voice, and dialling instructions in Braille for the blind. In exceptional circumstances, a lightweight headset can be supplied to replace the hand set but it may not be easy for a disabled person to position it.

Speech difficulties

Some disabilities, such as strokes or cerebral palsy, where brain damage has occurred, may cause speech difficulties. Although the intelligence may not necessarily be impaired, the ability to speak coherently is lost, and this can be very frustrating for the person trying to speak and the person trying to understand him.

Charts are available giving pictures of familiar objects which can be used for pointing out what is required, but similar charts together with a list of simple phrases clearly written can easily be made at home. Spelling boards can be used by those whose problem is mechanism of speech and whose concentration is good, but spelling everything out is slow and time-consuming. It is a very natural reaction to shout when talking to a person whose comprehension is slow, but this tendency should be controlled as it may increase the sense of panic and confusion.

Some people will be referred to a speech therapist to help them learn to speak again after illness or injury has damaged the powers of speech, but speech therapists are in very short supply and it may be necessary to practice at home with family and friends. Relaxation is often essential for re-learning speech, and this can be helped by accompanying action. For instance, the handicapped person and the person helping him can work together on a simple task, such as preparing vegetables for a meal, and talk about the vegetables by name, talk about the utensils used and so on. Slow clear speech from the helper and patience in awaiting response is invaluable, but not always easy to achieve. Nevertheless, the time spent in this way will reassure, and the positive results convince both that a speech defect does *not* imply mental impairment, for this is often a very real and deep fear. Practice times should be kept short and well within the capability of the affected person. Word games can also be used to provide equipment for practice, such as Scrabble and Keyword, but these should not be attempted until words and phrases can be identified.

CASE HISTORY

Miss G., a secretary, was increasingly troubled from her late thirties onwards with neck pain, for which she wore a light plastic collar, which gave support and helped to prevent painful and pain-provoking movements.

To cope with her work however, she had to make some modifications in the arrangement of her office equipment. The telephone was in constant use and holding the receiver to her ear was very tiring. She made enquiries about several types of holders with adjustable arms into which she could fix the receiver when making or receiving a call, but as her desk was next to a wall, she had two terry-clips fixed to the wall at the appropriate height and set at an angle, so that the receiver was near enough for her to hear and be heard but her hands were free, and her arms did not become fatigued.

When copy-typing she used a bookrest and placed it higher than normal so that she could work with her head well up, and for her clerical work she used a magnet board in conjunction with a book-rest.

At home she bought a high-backed chair which supported her head and tucked a small cushion into her neck. This used to slip until she stitched it to a slightly weighted chair-back which held it in place. She had her television on a higher table so that she could watch without strain, and for reading and writing she had a book-rest similar to her office one, on a mobile cantilever table which was adjustable in height and easily moved so that it could be pushed out of the way.

12

Leisure

DEVELOPING and maintaining social contact is a very difficult problem for the physically disabled, especially when mobility is restricted and it is necessary to rely on the services of another person to get out into the community. It is very important that every disabled person should make the effort to integrate, for segregation is not good at any level and for the physically disabled person it can complicate life by adding emotional problems to physical ones.

During the last two decades, the social climate has changed tremendously, and there is now more social awareness than ever before. Through the newspapers, radio and television, people are constantly being reminded of the needs of all sections of the community and there is a great reserve of goodwill towards those with problems of any kind. Disabled people should not be too independent nor too proud to accept this goodwill when it is offered, for it can lead to a happier and fuller life. They too have a part to play in the life of the community, for they can help able-bodied people to understand their needs, how to accept them, and when to help and not to help. In time they are accepted as individuals in their own right, and mix with their contemporaries socially and intellectually. Many famous, and not so famous, people come to mind who have not allowed their physical disability to quell their natural personality. Not least among these are the eloquent and forceful members of Parliament who, despite their disabilities, did so much to ensure the legislation of the Chronically Sick and Disabled Persons Act. Physical handicap is not an intellectual handicap, and a person who is mentally stimulating can overcome a physical disability. It may be trite to say "Where there's a will there's a way" but from the example set by so many disabled people we know that if one is determined to achieve an objective then the way can be found.

Often the greatest barrier to social life is the difficulty in getting to one's destination, and when there, the problems of doorways, stairs and toilet facilities. These problems are most difficult for the person in a wheelchair, and although more public buildings are being made accessible for wheelchair users by incorporating lifts, ramps, toilets and so on, there are still many buildings which do not have these facilities. If such places as public libraries, theatres, cinemas and public halls do not have such accommodation, then a little public relations work can go a long way towards achieving the objective. Letters to directors of social services for the area, local councillors, local authority committees dealing with public buildings, city architects, members of Parliament, and failing all else, newspapers, will all make people aware of the need.

It is difficult to suggest leisure activities specifically for handicapped people, for when one starts to look into the question in any depth, one realizes how wide and varied is the choice. Individual tastes are catered for as they are for non-handicapped people, indeed, most of the interests mentioned here are not only for the disabled. Many of the organizations will welcome anyone who shares their enthusiasm, but some of the local groups may have facilities which are not suitable for wheelchair users or the more severely disabled. If one is sufficiently interested however, it may be possible to seek support from one of the sources mentioned above so that facilities can be made available, or failing that for the club to be approached to ask if any of their members would visit to talk about their activities. Some of the groups mentioned are specifically for handicapped people, but they will provide the interest necessary to lead to wider participation.

The suggested leisure interests are grouped under headings for easy reference :

Collecting

Stamps. This is mainly an individual hobby but there are many local societies where enthusiasts can meet. If handling the stamps is a problem, adapted tweezers may help and the type of album should be carefully chosen from the various bindings available. One society has been formed specially to cater for the needs of the lone collector who may make pen friends and swop his stamps by post.
Invalid and Lone Collectors' Society, 79 Windsor Road, Cambridge.
Coins. This tends to be a more intellectual pursuit and meetings of the societies have lectures and exhibitions of an academic nature. Some parts of the country are rich in buried coins and local collections can be built up by digging around, either oneself or through friends.
British Association of Numismatic Societies, Secretary, P. A. Clayton, F.L.A., F.S.A., 6 Handside Close, Welwyn Garden City, Herts.
Folklore. There is still a rich heritage of old stories and legends, songs, rhymes, customs, superstitions and herbal remedies which will soon be forgotten unless they are recorded. A tape recorder would be a help in catching these memories in a permanent form, but time to listen and patience to draw out recollections are the essentials which may be the special attributes of a person whose other activities are limited. The Folklore Society is interested to hear of collectors of such material.
The Hon. Sec., The Folklore Society, c/o University College, London, Gower Street, London WC1E 6BT.

Games

Billiards and Snooker. Billiards is played in most social clubs and a prior enquiry to the games secretary would ensure that access was possible and that a player would be welcomed. Aids for steadying the cue are available and may also be made with a little ingenuity.
Table soccer and Subbutteo. This is a popular game among young people. It can be played on a table, the height fixed to suit the players, or on the floor. The two players each have a team of

"men" on bases which must be flicked to hit the ball and as in football the aim is to score goals and defend your own goal. There are local clubs which belong to a league and players take the names of famous soccer teams. Competitions range from local to national and international events.

Secretary, English Table Soccer Association, 22 Fassett Road, Kingston-on-Thames, Surrey.

Table tennis. Although the game requires speed and mobility, it is possible to achieve a high degree of skill which helps to overcome physical limitations. A wheelchair user can give a non-handicapped player a good game.

Chess. Physical disability is absolutely no hindrance in this game. There are many local clubs and several postal organizations. Magnetic sets are available to help those who have difficulty in co-ordination or pieces can have loops of wire to be moved with a mouthstick.

British Chess Federation, The Secretary, Juniper Cottage, South Park Crescent, Gerrards Cross, Bucks, SL9 8HJ.

British Correspondence Chess Association, 11 Greenway, Harold Park, Romford, Essex.

Cards. A card holder can be made of a block of wood with slits sawn in it, or a stiff brush can be used to support the cards. Packs are available in large sizes that are easy to see and to handle. There is a bridge club in most localities.

Jigsaws. For the keen puzzler there are several clubs which supply puzzles regularly.

Jigsaw Club, Miss R. Cockerton, 16 Bucks Avenue, Watford Heath, Herts.

Dominoes. There are large-sized dominoes, clearly marked and coloured, which are easier to see and to handle for those with clumsy hands.

Gardening

Much has been written on this subject, for it is increasingly recognized that gardening is one of the most healthful activities and can be taken up or continued in a modified form by almost anyone who has an interest in it. To bring it within the capacity of the disabled gardener, it is necessary to consider four points: the type, size and layout of the garden; the plants to be grown in it; the methods of cultivation; and the tools to use.

Every part of the garden should be accessible by non-slip firm paths, different levels being linked for the wheelchair user by ramps rather than steps, which should be shallow and accompanied by a handrail for the ambulant gardener. The tool shed and the greenhouse should be close to the path and the house. Raised beds may be built for growing small plants, especially salad vegetables

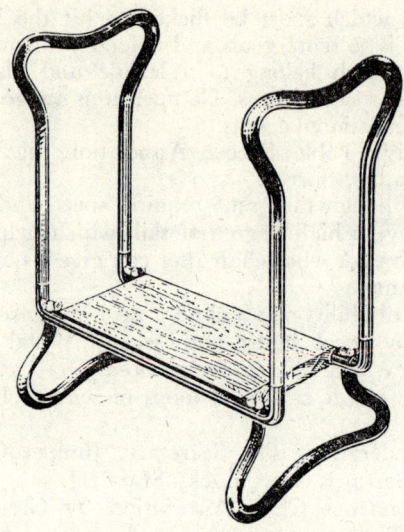

Easi-kneeler stool

and herbs or alpines some of which require careful trimming and can be appreciated better at close quarters.

Trouble-free plants such as hardy perennials, chosen to need no staking, ground-cover plants to smother annual weeds and un-interrupted stretches of lawn make for easy maintenance.

Methods of cultivation include the use of appropriate weed killers, mulches and fertilizers, as well as the choice of tools and equipment. In general, the wheelchair user needs a shorter handled tool than the ambulant gardener who for various reasons cannot bend. Some are very light, including a range of rockery tools which can be attached to full length handles. There are several aids for weeding and planting which do away with the need to stoop and much work can be done from a chair, or a garden stool which can also be used as a kneeler, having handles to help getting up and down.

One of the hazards of gardening is getting over tired. Work should be taken in small doses with regular rests and changes of job, varying the reach required, the level of the work and the strength needed. It is helpful to have resting places here and there in the garden—a special ledge on the raised bed, an old tub, a thick log or a formal seat. On the other hand, the disabled gardener may be able to spend more time on raising plants from seed, propagating by taking cuttings of all types and could do the pricking out and potting on for neighbours or friends.

The Easy Path to Gardening, published by Readers Digest, gives a most comprehensive account of all aspects of gardening for the disabled.

Handcrafts

Knitting and sewing aids. It is not easy to knit one-handed, but there are several holders which anchor one needle while the wool is manipulated with the sound hand. It is worthwhile to experiment with various aids, several of which are available from the British Red Cross Society. Only simple basic articles, such as blanket squares and garter stitch tea cosies, which require a small number of stitches and little weight on the needles should be attempted at first. Knitting machines can be operated successfully with limited movement, but a considerable degree of dexterity is required to cope with shaping. For household mending and sewing, an embroidery ring helps to hold the fabric taut. It can also be steadied by pinning it to the arm of a chair or on to the skirt. A "mushroom" can be fixed to a board and clamped to the chair or table. Self-threading needles save time and temper. Electric sewing machines can be adapted so that the control part is operated by the means best suited to the individual.

Model making. The local model shop will have information about branches of the societies for keen modellers. They meet regularly, hold exhibitions and exchange ideas and provide some technical advice.

Marquetry. Using the colours and grains of wood veneers for decoration is an old craft. The work is intricate and requires complete accuracy. Guide prints may be used but there is plenty of scope for original design. Equipment is minimal—a sharp, pointed knife, a cutting board, a simple press and, if possible, a mitre block for framing the work.

Tapestry. This well-known form of needlework is equally satisfying for men and women. In its finest form, used for evening bags, slippers, small pictures etc. it requires excellent sight and good co-ordination. However, the same basic method of covering canvas with stitches can be used to make chair seats, and, in its coarsest form, for rugs which are much less demanding but nevertheless can be endlessly varied.

Music and Arts

Singing. The voice is the instrument upon which most people can raise some kind of tune. Choral societies, choirs and groups of all kinds welcome enthusiastic contributors.

Instruments. Wind instruments, from the mouth organ to the clarinet, can be played even in bed! A guitar can be played in a wheelchair.

Piano playing. Certain types of weakness of the upper limbs can be overcome by the use of slings to support the forearm over the keys. A one-handed player can accomplish much, as Cyril Smith has shown, especially when playing duets or in concert with players of other instruments. The wheelchair pianist must be able to detach the footrests in order to approach the piano closely enough.

Painting. Mouth and foot painting are now well known and prove that extremely severe disability need not be a handicap to painting or drawing. Before using mouth-held aids of any kind, however, a dentist should be consulted so that the mouthpiece does not damage the teeth. For all who enjoy it, the hobby can provide the fullest outlet for self-expression, relaxation or stimulus. There are many classes and sketch clubs where the more mobile can learn to develop their techniques and exhibit their work.

Flower arranging. The National Association of Flower Arrangement Societies of Great Britain is a lively organization with clubs and societies which run classes and exhibitions all over the country. Very little equipment is required and there need be almost no expense in taking up this hobby, as utensils of all types can be used and one of the special satisfactions of the hobby is using whatever flower or leafy material is to hand for arrangements which give pleasure to the maker and to others. Searching for materials can be part of the activity and lead to greater interest and observation of plants and flowers. The NAFAS publishes *Tools and Equipment for Flower Arrangement* at a cost of five pence, plus postage, from Mrs. Kay Waterman, 25a Ridge Hill, Dartmouth, Devon.

National Association of Flower Arrangement Societies of Great Britain, 21a Denbigh Street, London SW1.

Pressed flowers. The best flowers for pressing are the small delicate, ones which grow wild. They can be collected for identification and a collection of common wild flowers can lead to a deeper interest and knowledge of the families of plants. Here again friends can help. The pressed flowers can also be arranged into pictures to be framed, on greeting cards and bookmarks etc.

A leaflet on the subject is obtainable from National Federation of Women's Institutes, 39 Eccleston Street, London SW1W 9NT.

Outdoor activities

Photography. This is another activity which can increase one's power of observation. Cheap cameras with the minimum of controls produce good pictures even for beginners and with practice, selection of the field of vision and understanding of light conditions can produce excellent results.

For those who find the controls difficult to handle, adaptations can be made such as a support on a universal joint for the camera and an extended lever to operate the shutter. To learn from one's mistakes and successes it is necessary to keep some kind of record of the conditions under which the picture was taken. Specialization in the choice of subjects taken makes for an interesting collection and greater skill. For example, a series of pictures of local gardens through the seasons, children playing quietly, results of hobbies such as models and flower arrangements.

Photography for the Disabled, Sec. Mrs. J. Sevase, 190 Secrett House, Ham Close, Ham, Richmond, Surrey.

Scouts. The Scout Association, 25 Buckingham Palace Road, London SW1 is deeply concerned to make the fun of scouting available to all, and especially to involve the boys with a handicap in the fullest possible range of activities with non-disabled boys. Skilled and experienced scouters help to integrate boys into local groups, and special camps are also organized for those who cannot take part in the regular troop camp. Boys work for badges and achievement grades and are encouraged to take responsibility to the fullest extent.

Guides. Girl Guide Association, 17 Buckingham Palace Road, London SW1 have extension activities for handicapped girls to include guiding by post, special camps and companies based on special schools.

Birdwatching. This can begin with crumbs on the window sill or bird table, but there are many nature reserves where by appointment with the secretary or warden a disabled person may obtain access to a hide or other vantage point. A keen watcher can make recordings of sightings of birds and bird behaviour which may contribute to research projects. Conservation of bird life depends greatly on amateur enthusiasm and help.

Royal Society for the Protection of Birds, The Lodge, Sandy, Beds.

Spectator sports. Football, rugby, hockey. Most clubs, large and small now provide good facilities for disabled spectators.

Reading and writing

Pen friends. Almost all the journals published by societies for specific disabilities carry advertisements for pen friends. It is also possible to make contact with like-minded people by writing to the journals connected with hobbies and leisure pursuits, such as the philatelic magazines, bird watching papers, etc.

Open University. The Open University combines the use of television, radio, and correspondence courses to provide an opportunity for adults to study for degrees in arts, sciences, mathematics, technology, social sciences and educational studies. Applications are welcomed from disabled people who are assessed for entry on their merits, and who are integrated with able-bodied students as far as possible. Some special facilities are available at the week's summer school held for each course and every effort is made to encourage participation by the disabled. The National Extension

College runs "gateway" courses for entry to the Open University, among many other courses for qualifications or purely for enjoyment.

The Open University, Admissions Office, P.O. Box 48, Bletchley, Bucks., National Extension College, 8 Shaftesbury Road, Cambridge, CB2 2BP.

Short story writing, articles etc. Writing for publication is very competitive, but a start can be made by taking a course run by a reputable correspondence school. The writer must be prepared for many rejections but persistence and practice may succeed, and in any case, if writing is pleasurable, it can be enjoyed for its own sake.

Correspondence colleges. The Association of British Correspondence Colleges Ltd. provides information on postal tuition available and co-operates with education authorities at all levels, giving advice and setting a standard of service to students.

Association of British Correspondence Colleges Ltd., 4-7 Chiswell Street, London EC1.

Social

Clubs. The local social services department and the British Red Cross Society can give information about clubs and facilities in general for the disabled. Most areas have social clubs for which transport is provided. There are also P.H.A.B. (Physically Handicapped and Able-bodied) youth clubs in many areas. Total integration of the physically handicapped into society is the philosophy of these clubs. PHAB, 30 Devonshire Street, London W1N 2AP.

Folk Dance and Song Society. Groups of this society flourish all over the country running folk evenings and festivals and encouraging all kinds of traditional activity. Instrumental and singing sessions are most popular and there are many camps and week-long courses where crafts can be learnt in a holiday setting.

English Folk Dance and Song Society, Cecil Sharp House, 2 Regents Park Road, London NW1 7AY.

Wheelchair dancing. The Spastic Society has pioneered the translation of square dancing patterns to wheelchair manoeuvre. A book of sets is published and information about the nearest facilities can be obtained from the Society, which runs courses for instructors.

Mr. A. S. T. Edwards, Physical Education Adviser, The Spastics Society, 88 Starvecion Close, Shipbourne Road, Tonbridge, Kent.

Entertaining. To entertain one's friends at home it is necessary only to offer pleasant company, but the facilities to make a cup of tea (and wash up) independently can be a source of pride to the host. An electric kettle filled on a trolley or tray with the milk and biscuits collected and tea bags in cups or a tea pot, strengthens the welcome and shows appreciation of the effort the guest has made to come. We want our friends to come because they want to see us however, and for some people it is not easy to keep up a flow of interesting conversation. It is very important to try to be outward looking and informed and involved in matters outside the immediate environment. T.V. and radio can help greatly to provide lively topics of discussion and comment, especially if some of the regular courses are followed and the subjects studied more deeply. Keeping up with newspapers and magazines, especially local ones, helps keep one in touch with events of widely varied interests, so that visitors can be entertained and amused. Home-made sweets, biscuits and cakes are a treat for anyone and many people enjoy a glass of home-brewed wine.

National Wine-Makers Association, Mr. P. Delmon, 95 Park Avenue North, Northampton NN3 HX.

Holidays. The Central Council for the Disabled with the British Red Cross Society produces annually a booklet on "Holidays for the Handicapped". This contains a great deal of information on holidays arranged purely for disabled people, guest houses run for disabled people and hotels and guest houses which have some facilities which are helpful. The A.A. guide gives information for disabled about its recommended accommodation, and social services departments have details of any specially adapted caravans there may be in their area.

Sports

Wheelchair basketball. This sport is encouraged in special units and there is now a league in which nine clubs compete. More would be welcomed by the National Wheelchair Basketball League which is affiliated to the Amateur Basketball Association. National Wheelchair Basketball League, Mr. H. Searle, Hon. Sec. c/o Education Department, Rampton Hospital, Retford, Notts.

Swimming clubs. Swimming is one of the most stimulating and satisfying forms of physical exercise, and since gravity is eliminated provides for some people freedom of movement obtainable in no other way. If participation in the local pool is impossible in the normal way, it is possible in most areas to find a club for the disabled, which has access to a pool for regular sessions where assistance and coaching is available, and the temperature of the water appropriate.

National Association of Swimming Clubs for the Disabled, The Hon. Sec., 93 The Downs, Harlow, Essex.

Association of Swimming Therapy, Mr. J. MacMillan, 24 Arrows Road, London N11.

Shooting. There is no reason, normally, why a disabled person should not participate in this sport, although he may not always be able to take a full part. There is a competition rule specifically for physically handicapped shooters which allows them to apply for permission to assume a special position or use modified equipment. Pistol shooting is probably the most suitable form though a rifle can be fired from a wheelchair. Air pistol and rifle shooting are less expensive, and no Firearm Certificate is required for an air pistol. The secretary of the National Small-Bore Rifle Association will put enquirers in touch with a local club.

The Secreary, Codrington House, 113 Southwark Street, London SE7.

Archery. This sport is used in hospitals and the Grand National Archery Society has several physiotherapist coaches who ensure that disabled people receive the instruction suited to their disability. Great physical strength is not required but wheelcchair archers must be prepared to rely on help for the retrieval of their arrows.

The Secretary, Grand National Archery Society, 20 Broomfield Road, Chelmsford, Essex.

Fishing. Access to the stretch of water suitable for the disabled angler may be the greatest hindrance. Aids of various kind have been designed for holding the rod and for baiting and removing the catch. The National Anglers' Council can help in putting the enquirer in touch with the local club fishing the most suitable water.

The Secretary, The National Anglers' Council, 17 Queen Street, Peterborough.

Riding. The Riding for the Disabled Association, National Equestrian Centre, Kenilworth, Warminster, has 130 groups which give free weekly sessions when the rider is taught and assisted by up to three helpers, including trained professional staff. Riders are mostly children, but adults can participate. This activity may give a sense of achievement and independence in mobility totally lacking in all other circumstances. Not least is the satisfaction of being high up in the world, especially for the wheelchair user! British Sports Association for the Disabled, Stoke Mandeville Stadium, Harvey Road, Aylesbury, Bucks.

CASE HISTORY

Mr. F has been a keen gardener all his life. During the past ten years he has had chronic bronchitis, so that he tires very quickly and becomes breathless even on slight exertion. However, this condition has come on gradually and Mr. F was determined to meet his handicap realistically and above all to carry on with his interest in gardening. To achieve this he adapted and re-designed his garden to be more labour saving, and made a careful Christmas list of tools so that he could gradually acquire more suitable and labour saving ones.

The toolshed and small greenhouse were at the far end of the garden and his first move was to resite the shed nearer to the house. His son helped him with the heavy work of laying down new footings and making new paths in the garden. They used concrete finished with a non-slip surface, and made more paths in the vegetable garden, so cutting down the open ground and making the working of the remainer easier. Near the house they paved an area which linked the toolshed and the site for the new, slightly larger greenhouse, taking care to make a grass path accessible to the shed where the mower would be kept. The width of the flower border was reduced and grassed over, to give a larger uninterrupted area of lawn for easy mowing.

In planning the re-shaped borders, more use was made of flowering shrubs heathers and other ground cover plants.

Mr. F was undecided as to the best type of mower to have but he made sure there was a power point in the toolshed which could be used for a mains-powered mower or for recharging a battery-powered one.

The other major item was a new light wheelbarrow with a tool-rack attached to it. He had often taken a kitchen chair out so that he could sit to do some of the light forking or hoeing, but he wanted to get an easy-kneeler stool for its dual purpose value. He also gradually equipped with long-handled cultivators which he chose with cranked handles because these were easiest to control.

Lastly, he had the lean-to greenhouse erected by the house. Here he was able to extend his interest in chrysanthemums and tomatoes as well as grow vegetables and flowering plants from seed. With a small amount of heat from an electric fan heater he was able to start things early and propagate many plants for his friends. The greenhouse was near enough to the house to allow him to work out there even in the winter, when the weather was not fit for him to be out of doors.

Housing and Access

PLANNING accommodation for disabled people as though they were a homogeneous population is an almost impossible task. The needs of a single disabled person differ from those of a disabled man with an able-bodied wife, or a disabled housewife needing to care for her family, and the person using a wheelchair will present differing problems again. But, above all, the disabled person requires a *home* in all its essentials, like that of any able-bodied individual.

It is said that an Englishman's home is his castle, meaning a place where he can pursue his activities as he pleases, in privacy when he wishes, independently, and without interference; where he can collect his own possessions, create his own setting, and take a pride in it; a place to which he can invite his friends to share his pleasure in it, and a base from which he can set out and return to; a shelter where he is secure.

The basic activities of daily living have already been mentioned, and the ability to cope with them depends to a large extent on the architectural features of the dwelling which is intended to be home. For a single individual this may be a bed-sitter, a flat, or a house. Whatever it is, it should be an environment which will work for him and yet conform as nearly as possible to the accepted norm of his social circle.

For the disabled member of a family, it is important that the home satisfies their needs also, and that when modifications have to be made, they are the result of joint planning and agreed compromises. Any family home changes in size as children come, grow up and go away, and this fluctuation can be anticipated and turned to good account in meeting the requirements of disability. For instance, an extension may be built to give adolescents more study and play room, and be used later to accommodate a relative or other person to give extra help as increasing age makes independence difficult.

Space requirements and special housing

Usually, more than the average amount of space needs to be allotted for circulation and access, particularly in the bathroom, lavatory and kitchen, and to compensate for this, houses need to be built with less garden space or with fewer bedrooms.

Local authorities have the power to make appropriate provision for specially designed housing for disabled people, but it is not always easy for the extra expenditure involved on such housing to be justified in the face of social pressures arising from long housing lists.

When a house does not fulfil the needs of the disabled person living in it, there are several courses of action open to him. Aids and appliances can be used to mitigate the disadvantages of the house; new equipment can be installed such as hoists, lifts, ramps and showers; the house can be altered structurally; or he can decide to find more suitable accommodation.

Before embarking on any of these courses of action, it is essential to seek advice from the doctor and health services, for through them and with the advice of the domiciliary occupational therapist, every effort will be made to seek a sensible solution to the problems.

It is important to bear in mind that any alteration to existing accommodation should not be so drastic that other members of the family will be inconvenienced to a great degree, for in such a situation tensions develop in the home.

The following suggestions may make life a great deal easier for the physically disabled member of the family.

Access

Ideally, the entrance to the house should be by a firm path or roughed up concrete or tarmacadam, which should be designed so that one can get from the front door to the back door of the house. Many people use paving stones or gravel for paths, but these are not suitable for they tend to be difficult and dangerous for anyone with slight instability when walking. Paving stones tend to become uneven and can be very slippery in frosty weather, and gravel paths cannot be negotiated by the person in a wheelchair. The width of the path should be between 3 feet 6 inches and 4 feet preferably with a turning area so that the person in a wheelchair can be accompanied.

If steps at the front and back door are too high to be easily negotiated, it may be possible to build another half step which is wide enough and shallow enough to give a good area for balancing whilst turning the door handle or locking the door. When more than one step is involved at the entrance to the house, a handrail should be fixed at a convenient height for support, for all steps and stairs can be hazardous for an elderly or physically disabled person.

For the wheelchair user, the approach to the house should be by way of a gentle sloping ramp made of concrete, with a gradient no steeper than one in twelve (and preferably shallower) and with a level platform immediately in front of the door, so that it can be negotiated by the person in a self-propelling wheelchair. There should be no threshold, the door being protected by stormboarding against the weather with a porch or canopy overhead.

Doors

Both front and back doors should have the fittings sited so that they are accessible to the disabled member of the family. Door locks both internal and external and a letterbox with a retaining cage or tray should be within easy reach. Light switches for internal and external lights should be immediately available inside the front door at a convenient height, and light should provide clear illumination of the approach to the house, front door and hallway.

Door locks sometimes present problems for the person with weak or stiff grip and various locks have been designed to overcome this difficulty. Some of the Yale type locks have a lever handle for ease of turning, or specially designed magnetic locks so that a key slips in easily to turn. In some instances, the existing key can be smoothed so that it is easier to insert. If additional grip is needed for a Yale lock handle it has been found that the type of rubber tip which fits over broom handles will fit over the key handle like a big thimble. An additional handle on the door is advisable for pulling or pushing the door open.

Garage doors

Garage doors may be particularly difficult for a physically disabled person to use, because they are very heavy. In many instances, a car-port may be the best solution to this problem. Electrically operated garage doors are available which are controlled by pushbutton switches from either the house or the drive. A more sophisticated device is a remote control unit which is effective up to thirty feet and is powered by dry batteries which can be fitted into a convenient position in the car with the receiver unit mounted in the garage. Some weather protection between house and garage is desirable, especially for wheelchair users.

Internal doors

Where possible, all doors should have a minimum width of 2 feet 9 inches, and where a door serves a room in which circulation space is required it may be advisable to install a sliding door. There are many designs of these available but particular care should be taken to ensure that the door width will be sufficient if a wheelchair is used. The tracks of the sliding door can be installed so that the whole width of the doorway is left clear, apart from the four inches required for the handle. When a wheelchair is used it is inadvisable to have a sunken ground track because it may impede wheelchair access and grit and dust will accumulate in it, therefore a top hung track is preferable. Sliding doors which open from the centre and part to each side may be suitable in some cases, such as between two rooms. Cushion edging can be fitted to prevent draught and noise, and silent tracking is available for some doors.

Lever handles are preferable to door knobs for they are much easier to turn. If ball catches are fitted to doors a door-handle or "pulls" will be needed. For the wheelchair user, a horizontal rail or a doorhandle at the hinge side makes closure easier.

It may be found that if a door is re-hung it will open from a more convenient angle. But if none of these adaptations are suitable, it may be possible to instal a hinged door which will fold in half before folding back, for this takes less space and requires less manoeuvring than a full size door.

If possible, bathroom and lavatory doors should be hung so that they open outwards to make extra space in these rooms, and access easier should emergency arise. For reasons of safety, locking these doors from the inside should be discouraged, for with a little consideration by other members of the family and some indication that the lavatory is occupied, this should not be necessary.

Rising butt hinges which allow doors to close automatically are often helpful.

Windows

It is difficult to generalize about the most suitable types of window, for each type available may present problems. The modern type of louvre window can be controlled easily for opening by a drop rod, cord or winding handle, but will present problems with cleaning, and in some situations can be draughty. Windows which are controlled by a pivot for opening are relatively easy to control, easier to clean, but more difficult to curtain, and can be hazardous at ground level outside. Sash windows are also difficult because they involve reaching upwards to open and to lock. Side hung casements with two-handed action to open and fasten are also difficult, and cause obstruction sometimes at ground floor level. The most satisfactory type of window will depend very much on the type of disability.

A useful guide when new windows are to be installed is that the window sill should not be higher than two feet to a maximum of two feet six inches in a leisure room, such as a sitting room, so it is possible for the seated person to look out.

Stairs

Many elderly and physically disabled people have great difficulty in getting up and down stairs. The majority of these can be helped by the simple measure of installing rails so that there is support on both sides of the stairs. These rails should be

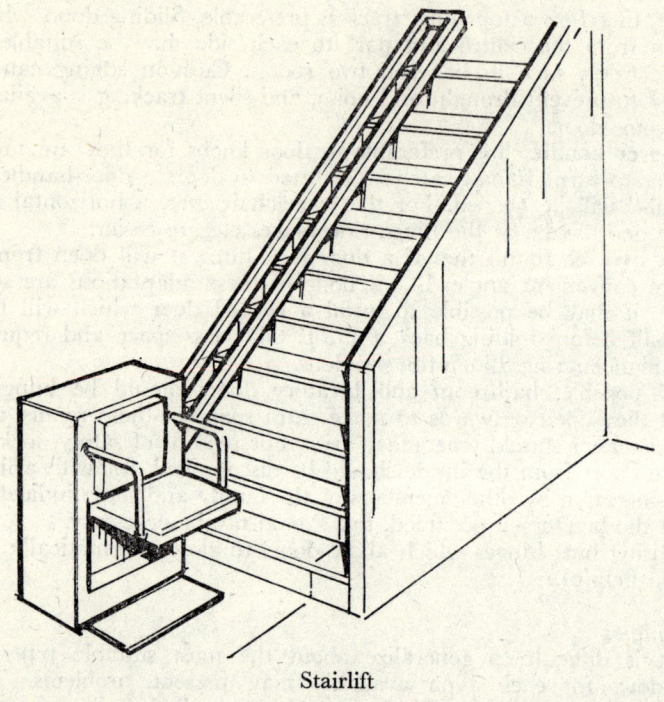

Stairlift

continuous and of a convenient size so that they can be gripped firmly for support. If disability is not too severe it may be possible to get up the stairs by sitting up them, rather than walking up.

It is always advisable to try to organize the day so that it is not necessary to go up and downstairs more than absolutely necessary.

For the more severely disabled, it may be possible to instal a mechanical stair lift which will enable the person to sit or stand on a platform which will go up or down either automatically by push-button or hand controlled by an attendant. These are somewhat sophisticated appliances and are therefore rather expensive. They are mostly designed for straight flights of stairs, but some are available which will operate on a curved staircase. Some of them are also designed to carry a person sitting in a wheelchair. Purchase of the stairlifts is available on instalments, and in some cases, local authorities have purchased them and will allow them to be hired. It is advisable to check the various makes and seek advice from the social services department who will advise on the most suitable type before such an expensive piece of equipment is purchased.

An alternative method of reaching the upper floors of the house is by installing a lift. There are many small domestic lifts now on the market which are suitable for the average size house. They can be installed in the corner of a sitting room or a hallway, and although they obviously take up a certain amount of space, they may be considered an acceptable alternative to living entirely at ground floor level. Some of these lifts can be operated by hand controls and others are electrically operated. The smaller ones are only 3 feet 6 inches by 3 feet wide. Before purchasing it is essential to check that it is large enough to accommodate the person *sitting in* his wheelchair, and that the controls can be reached easily. If a lift is installed, adequate precautions should be taken if young children are in the house to ensure that it is not used without supervision.

A hoist lift, which can be lowered through a trap door in the ceiling, or down the stair well, may be a suitable method of transferring from first to ground floor level. However, this way may prove more suitable for a slightly built young person rather than an older person who may not like the sensation of being lowered in the sling.

Circulation space and floor covering

The person who is able to walk, even a little, will prefer small spaces and narrow rooms with walls and solid fittings within easy reach, so that they can be used for support, and non-slip flooring so that sticks, crutches or walking frames can be used safely.

On the other hand, the wheelchair user will need plenty of space for manoeuvring, with a turning circle of at least five feet. Cork or plastic flooring should be used, or close fitting short pile carpet so that the wheels of the chair will not get caught in the edges of mats or carpets (which are also a hazard for unsteady walkers).

If the available space is limited, it may be possible to alter the house by interconnecting rooms at ground floor level and dispensing with corridors as much as possible. Wheelchair users cannot negotiate sharp right angle turns from narrow corridors.

Extensions

If it becomes impractical to continue to use the upper floors of the house, then alterations to ground floor accommodation may be considered. It is important that lavatory and washing facilities are available downstairs, and that there is sufficient circulation space if a wheelchair is used.

In the average semi-detached house, it is possible to make a variety of adaptations to the existing structure to include these facilities if necessary. Many local authorities will advise and, in some cases, provide a grant for alterations to be made. Each

131

application is considered individually, and will depend on what is needed and what is structurally possible.

For many people, the installation of sliding doors or folding doors between the downstairs rooms will improve facilities for living on one level with the minimum inconvenience, especially if a lavatory is accessible on the ground floor. If the door connecting the living area with the kitchen is also made wider it will be easier for the person in a wheelchair to have complete access to all the necessary rooms. The addition of a purpose-built extension, such as those available in modular form, could add to the leisure area.

If it is necessary to instal bathroom and lavatory facilities, a single prefabricated unit is available which is installed on a concrete base and linked with existing water and drainage systems.

Equipment

Much of the equipment that can be installed in the home to make life easier, such as hoists, showers and shower seats, toilet adaptations and so on, is dealt with in the chapters relating to these particular activities, but it is particularly relevant to mention again the installation of grab rails, usually made of metal or wood, which can be fixed throughout the house wherever extra support is needed. The position of these will depend on the type of disability and the individual activities and habits of the person, but as a general guide they are particularly necessary wherever steps are involved, in bathrooms, lavatories, kitchens and corridors.

People with poor balance tend to grab fixed objects to steady themselves, and if the object is neither fixed nor stable, accidents often result. All rails should be fixed firmly to the wall and not just screwed to the wall plaster. Different methods of attachment are required for different types of wall construction:

Timber studding plaster board: Rails can be fixed to uprights or cross bearers. If these are not in the right place then battens ($1\frac{1}{8}$ inch minimum diameter) can be fixed to the partition by screws or bolts.

Patent partitions: Rails attached to these must be sandwiched with a batten each side, bolted through, and the heads and nuts recessed into the wood. The battens should be long enough to distribute the pressure over a wide area.

Concrete blocks or breeze blocks: These can be drilled with the holes off-square to produce a dove-tailed effect and plastic plugs (of the correct size) and stout screws used to secure the rail.

Lightweight hollow blocks: Toggle bolts can sometimes be used, or one or more blocks removed and replaced with a solid block of brickwork bedded with mortar and securely wedged with slate.

Brick walls : Battens should be secured using No. 10 screws with
   1½ inches into the brickwork, and in pairs not more than 16
   inches apart.
Stonework : The soft plaster must be removed and the battens
   fitted on to uneven stone surfaces to ensure adequate beaming
   of the wood on the stone. Drill and screw as for brickwork.
Salamander blocks : These may be replaced by solid bricks as
   for light hollow blocks above.

For exceptional weightbearing, coach screws and Rawl bolts are
recommended for securing bearers or equipment. It may be necessary to bolt right through the wall.

If moisture is likely to form round any fitting it is essential
to use brass screws.

Rails fixed in lavatory and bathroom should be at the most
convenient height for the user, which is determined by practical
trial. Horizontal and vertical rails are often more appropriate than
slanting ones, and if a sloping rail is used then it *must* have a non-
slip surface. In general, the preferred diameter of grab rails is
1¼ inches to 1½ inches.

Components and fittings

The majority of people take the standard fittings in their homes
for granted, but for many people with weak or stiff grip or tremor,
the door handles, window catches, light switches, taps, electric
switches and outlet sockets in their homes present real problems.

The British Red Cross Society publish a very useful booklet of
aids for these activities, and this can be purchased from the nearest
branch of the Society.

Tap turning devices can be made by the home handyman,
and certain commercially made taps are much easier to use than
others.

Practical trials for the siting of electric light switches and sockets
will save much trouble and expense; as a general guide sockets
should not be placed on the skirting board but at a height between
2 feet 6 inches and 3 feet 6 inches from the floor, this is also a
convenient height for electric switches. Double outlet sockets
should be used rather than adaptors and a provision of as many
sockets as possible, for instance by the installation of a ring main,
will make it unnecessary to trail wires across the room which constitutes a hazard. Suitably designed switches, such as rocker
switches, require the minimum amount of effort to use. Good light-
ing is very important in every home, and all stairs, steps and
corridors should be well lit, with two way switches in bedrooms
and on stairways. If table lamps are used they should have a
weighted base so that they cannot be tipped and knocked over
very easily.

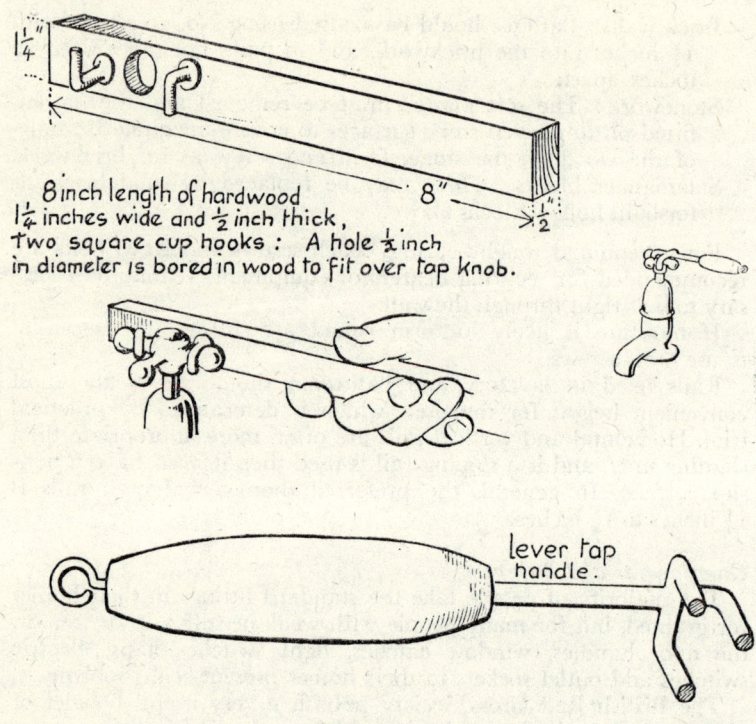

8 inch length of hardwood
1¼ inches wide and ½ inch thick,
Two square cup hooks : A hole ¼ inch
in diameter is bored in wood to fit over tap knob.

lever tap
handle.

Tap turners

Many people find that changing an overhead light bulb is difficult. This can be overcome by rise and fall light fittings, although they are rather expensive. It is usually advisable to have an alternative light in the room, such as a table or bedside lamp, so that the person who is unable to change a bulb will not have to sit in the dark until someone can do this for them.

Heating

Many elderly and disabled people have poor circulation and the maintenance of a reasonable background temperature is very important for their health and comfort.

Central heating is not installed in a large percentage of homes in the U.K., but various forms of unit heating are available. Many elderly people prefer to use a coal fire, but this does present many problems. A fireguard is essential and great care should be taken when placing fuel on the fire. A trolley can be used to transport the coal receptacle and cleaning material to the fireplace, but ashes should not be removed while they are still hot. Fuel should be stored as near to the house as possible.

Electric convector heaters are particularly suitable for unit heating because they can be obtained in both large and small capacity outputs. They should not be placed in any position where they are likely to be knocked over, and should be as close as possible to the outlet socket to avoid trailing wires. Fan heaters are also safe and efficient. Oil convector heaters should be avoided by physically disabled and elderly people because they may be difficult to fill with fuel and to light, and if sited in a room where there is a lot of activity they could prove a hazard for the person using a walking aid or a wheelchair.

Electric storage radiators are particularly suitable for background heating. Because they can be purchased separately they may be the most practical form of central heating for an established house, the installation being comparatively easy. They are very heavy and difficult to move, but can be easily switched off or boosted in extremes of weather, thus making them economical to use.

In a newly built or specially designed house, ducted warm air is very suitable for there are no hot radiators and the air circulates through small grills in the walls. Underfloor heating is used in many houses but it is not always satisfactory as it cannot be reduced or boosted quickly enough to cope with the changes in the weather.

Doors and windows should be insulated against draughts as much as possible to prevent heat loss.

Emergencies

The fuse box and isolating switches, gas meter and main water inlet control valve should be easily accessible and regularly tested to ensure that they are working efficiently. Without such precautions the chances of an emergency are greatly increased. The danger in an emergency for a person who is slow moving or severely disabled cannot be over emphasized.

Apparatus to deal with emergencies should be available for every handicapped person, together with a means of summoning help. Easily manipulated fire extinguishers, asbestos blankets for smothering fire, and a well stocked first aid box are essential in every home. A telephone should be installed in every home where a member of the family is severely disabled, together with an intercom system. Advice on this can be obtained from the Post Office telecommunications department, and in some cases it may be possible to obtain financial assistance from the social services towards the installation of a telephone for a severely disabled person. (See Communication, Chapter 11.)

Where an old person, or old people are living without support from a younger person, it is a good idea to have instructions clearly written and accessible describing the position of electric and gas main inlet, and water stop cock and other relevant information, in case a neighbour is called on for help in an emergency.

Alternative housing

If the decision is made to seek an alternative and more suitable home, it is advisable to give thought to the difficulties that may be experienced in settling in a new neighbourhood, neighbours and old friends will be missed and new social contacts take time to build up. The new home should not be too isolated and good facilities such as transport, shops, libraries and, if necessary, schools, should be nearby. It is worthwhile to try to find out if the neighbours are sociable, for this can be very important.

Local authority housing committees may be approached to provide a bungalow or ground floor flat, but this will usually involve a waiting period. If one is living in privately owned accommodation, or seeking to purchase a new home for the first time, the local authority can still be called upon for advice and assistance with necessary layout and alterations, and the most suitable method of dealing with these. Application should be made through the director of social services.

If the new home is to be a purpose-built bungalow, it is very important that the architect should be made fully aware of the likely areas of difficulty, and should seek advice from medical personnel in order that he can design the most suitable type of dwelling for the person's needs. The positioning of doors, accessibility, manoeuvring space, steps, and toilet facilities are all extremely important. The design and placement of the furniture will also need to be considered.

Access to public buildings

Some disabled and elderly people compensate for the architectural barriers and restrictions which they met by developing new skills and techniques to overcome or circumvent them, but many more become frustated and restricted, giving up rather than trying to overcome the difficulties involved when venturing out into the community.

Until recently, the special needs of the physically disabled have received scant attention. But, with the advent of the Chronically Sick and Disabled Persons Act, much time and effort is being spent by architects, social workers and others interested in the welfare of these members of the community in planning for their integration into everyday life.

The British Standard Institute's Code of Practice (CP 96) deals with the general considerations of access for the disabled to public buildings, and gives the lead for future developments. With these standards, and with the active influence of voluntary organisations, most public buildings now endeavour to incorporate some modifications so that they may be used by those with a physical disability.

Often it is the lack of information about available facilities rather than the lack of facilities which constitutes the handicap. Appropriate signposting can be a considerable help, and is now widely used. Many towns and cities now provide special guidebooks for the disabled, and these are extremely useful when planning a route or a tour, for they eliminate much time-wasting.

Information on how to obtain copies of the guidebooks will be given by Access for the Disabled, 34 Eccleston Square, London SW1.

Guides for the areas, towns and cities given below are available. Aberdeen, Battle, Bexhill and district, Bakewell, Bath, Bradford, Birmingham, Cambridge, Canterbury, Chelmsford, Chesterfield, Colchester, Coventry, Crawley, Dublin, Eastbourne, Edinburgh, Exeter, Falmouth, Glasgow, Grantham, Hastings and St. Leonards, Ipswich, Lambeth, Leeds, Lewisham, London, Luton, Manchester, Norwich, Oxford, Perthshire, Plymouth, Richmond, Scotland, Sheffield, Shrewsbury, Southampton, Southport, Swansea, Taunton, Torbay, Wallingford, York.

One of the major problems in designing public biuldings with disabled people in mind is that, in general, more space is required for manoeuvring and for access than it is for the able-bodied. It is this extra space that is so difficult to provide, for extra space means extra cost as far as building is concerned, and the most that can be done in many instances it to plan so that equivalent or equal opportunity is given to the disabled, for the well adjusted person will realise that the environment must be planned predominantly for the largest section of the community.

Sources of information
British Standard Code of Practice CP96. Part I. General Recommendations. Access for the disabled to buildings. This document is concerned specifically with the needs of disabled people, but it can also provide information on improving the convenience of any building used by non-disabled or elderly people, for it represents a standard of good practice. CP96 is available from the British Standards Institute on application.
American Standard Specifications for making buildings and facilities accessible to, and useable by, the physically disabled. Published in 1961 by the American Standards Association it contains recommendations for making all public buildings and facilities accessible to and functional for, the physically handicapped, without loss of function, space and facility for the general public.

This is an essential reference work for all architects of public buildings, institutions and domestic buildings used by the disabled. This is also available from the British Standard Institute.

Designing for the Disabled by Selwyn Goldsmith. The second edition of this book, published in 1967 by the Royal Institute of British Architects, is different in many ways from the first edition printed in 1963. The first edition deals primarily with domestic buildings, whereas the second edition gives more emphasis to the design of public buildings.

Available from leading booksellers.

Access for the Disabled. Sponsored by the Central Council for the Disabled, 34 Ecleston Square, London SW1. This is a national campaign to make public buildings and facilities accessible for the disabled.

Planning for the disabled people in an urban environment. Central Council for the Disabled, 1969.

An introduction to domestic design for the disabled, by Felix Walter, F.R.I.B.A., available from the Disabled Living Foundation.

14

Severe Disability

SOME people are obviously very severely disabled. For example, there are a number of people who have contracted poliomyelitis and who are virtually paralysed; others have suffered road accidents or other injuries and have sustained a broken neck but yet survived, although they also may be left with almost complete paralysis from the shoulders down. The loss of both legs, either in an accident or from disease is also a very severe disability. Some children with severe forms of spina bifida or cerebral palsy are also grossly handicapped, and people with progressive crippling nervous disorders, such as motor neurone disease or the late stages of severe multiple sclerosis may also become severely disabled.

Severe disability means that the person is, for most of the

activities of daily life, dependent upon other people. A major group of severely disabled people are those who, because of weakness, are unable to feed themselves or manage their own personal toilet. Another group are dependent upon artificial aids to maintain life, as for example, those people who have had severe poliomyelitis involving the respiratory muscles, which means that they have to rely on a breathing machine such as an iron lung, tank respirator, a rocking bed, or cuirasse to help them breathe. The third largest group are those with severe progressive arthritis who become increasingly unable to manage their personal care. But the severity of the disability, and the degree of the handicap are dependent upon many factors, of which the actual diesase process is only one.

The use of respiratory aids such as iron lungs has been known for a very long time, but it is only in recent years that many other mechanical aids have become available for use by the severely disabled. Perhaps the greatest revolution has been the provision of powered indoor wheelchairs which enable a very severely disabled person to have some independence of mobility, providing that his surroundings are suitable for him to negotiate a powered chair.

Wheelchairs have been discussed at some length in Chapters 2 and 3, but it is important to emphasize again that powered wheelchairs can be prescribed for any person who cannot propel himself by any other means, or if propelling himself is detrimental to his disability. In order to obtain a powered indoor chair, an independent medical assessment has to be made by one of the doctors appointed by the Department of Health and Social Security, such as an Appliance Medical Officer at one of the Artificial Limb and Appliance Centres. It is very important that the assessment for the powered chair should be made in a practical way, because there are different designs of chairs, and different designs of controls, and it needs an expert to match the type of chair and the type of controls with the disability of the person concerned. For this reason, amongst others, not only is the disabled person seen by the Appliance Medical Officer, but also one of the technical officers who work at the Appliance Centre. He will visit the home to make sure that it will be possible for the chair to be manoeuvred, whether there are appropriate power points so that the batteries which operate the chair can be re-charged at night, and whether the person will be able to operate the controls of such a chair.

From the point of view of the person concerned, there are two main aspects of the powered wheelchair. One is the seating. Many severely disabled people are unable to sit upright in the normal fashion and some have severe spinal deformities which require special cushioning, or a reclining back rest. Some people have been provided with powered chairs in which they can lie on their back, or on their stomach, and still drive their powered chair independently around their home. The other main feature of a powered chair which will be of particular concern for the disabled person is the control system. Such chairs are usually operated by small switches or levers, but most of the chairs can be adapted so that they can be controlled by microswitches. These can be operated by finger movement, head movement, foot movement, or any other movement which the person is able to make. They can also be controlled by sucking and blowing through a small plastic tube operating air switches. Thus, it is almost possible to say that nowadays, provided the person can control his breathing, or has a little movement available even in one finger, and he lives in a house which is suitable for a powered wheelchair, he will be able to obtain some degree of independent movement.

Beds

Most severely disabled people naturally spend a great deal of time in bed, and many of them require special beds. Some of these are now available so that they can be raised or lowered to make it easier to nurse, and to get the person in and out of bed. Others tilt the person from side to side to change the areas of the body which are under pressure, reducing the chances of the skin breaking and pressure sores occurring. Electrically operated beds

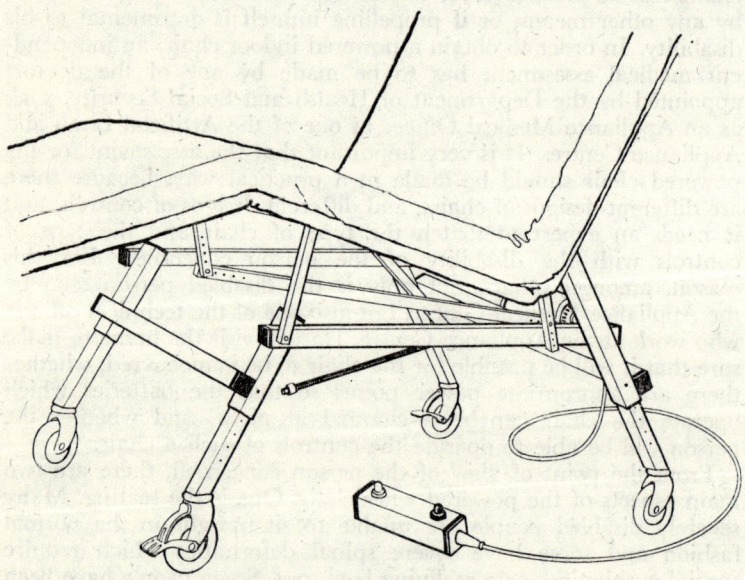

Electrically operated bed

on which the head can be raised and the foot lowered by push button control enable the person to be transferred from the lying to the sitting position. Some of these can be operated by the person themselves, thus avoiding some of the problems which arise from disturbing other members of the household at night. Some people who use these beds are able to dress themselves by using the mechanism which enables them to sit upright, which they would be unable to do in a normal bed.

As an additional facility for the severely disabled, particularly for those who have some impairment of their sensation, it may be necessary to instal special mattresses on the bed which are electrically operated so that they change their shape continually and gradually, thus varying the pressure areas. "Flotation" beds and beds with water mattresses are now being designed for use in the home for the very severely disabled with pressure area problems. For the less severely disabled, sleeping on natural sheepskins which have been medically prepared will also prevent the development of pressure sores, and some of the discomforts which arise from spending a lot of time lying or sitting in bed. One of the most uncomfortable, and frequently one of the most dangerous things in a disabled person's bed is a rubber air ring. All too often this causes localized pressure, and the skin breaks down, instead of relieving the pressure as intended.

Hoists

One of the big problems with severely disabled people who are unable to do a great deal for themselves, is the difficulty of getting them in and out of bed. This manoeuvre may be necessary to get them into their powered chair, or to get them out of bed for toilet or bathing. For the purpose there are a number of different hoists available which can usually be obtained through the local authority social services department. Hoists are described in detail in Chapter 2 but it is worth repeating that for the severely disabled there are suitable electric hoists which run on a track which will go over the bed and enable them to be lifted and tracked across on to a commode, a wheelchair or their powered wheelchair. Some of these hoists can be fitted to the ceiling of the house, usually by the local authority. But there are others which have an independent framework so that they can be moved to a different house if it is necessary to move. Once again, the controls of electric hoists are the part of the machinery which is of particular interest to the disabled person, and these are very simple. Usually they consist of small switches which are operated by strings which hang down from the hoist and many very severely disabled people are able to operate the hoist themselves if they

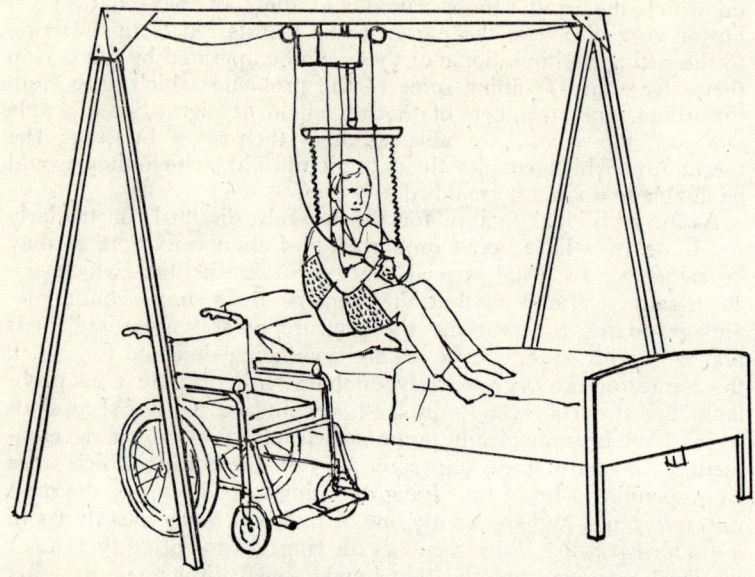

Electric hoist on gantry. Standard slings are slipped under the thighs and back, hooked on to chains and the motor operated by light pull on the cord. Hoist travels along gantry by pulling on rope which passes over pulleys at each side of the hoist

are able to place the slings around their body, but even if they are unable to do so, these appliances are a considerable help to the family in lifting procedures.

Special control appliances

In recent years, a number of appliances have been invented which are designed to enable severely disabled people to control a number of appliances such as warning buzzers, the lights of their room, their radio, television, telephone, electric typewriter, or even open and shut their front door and draw the curtains. Basically, it must be possible to control each activity by some form of electric motor, and then all that is necessary for the disabled person to do is to operate an electric switch. All the outlets are controlled from one central control panel, and by controlling one microswitch by muscular movement, or by sucking and blowing, the person can select whichever apparatus he wishes to operate. For example, there may be a control to switch on the radio, another to turn it off, a further control to operate the tuning device, and a fourth one to operate the volume. By operating one single switch it is possible to select the control and allow the control to work until it has done the job required.

Some of these devices are now being provided by the Department of Health for those people who have the ability and the motivation to use this type of apparatus, and have gone past any acute stage of their illness so that they are likely to remain severely disabled for some time. Particular consideration is given to those people who are likely to be left alone for long periods, and therefore need to control their own environment to some extent, and thus gain some level of independence. Some of the people who use these devices are able to work, using the machine to operate a typewriter, tape recorder and telephone. Once again, provided that a person has some slight movement of his finger, arm, foot or head, or is able to control his breathing, he may be able to operate this complex device and have some control over his surroundings. Often the most important part of the appliance is the alarm system and the telephone control. If it is possible to operate these then it means that he can be left for periods of time. Although they are very expensive and complicated, it may well be preferable both for the person concerned and for his family, if he can be supported in this way so that he continues to live at home rather than in an institution.

CASE HISTORY

James was eighteen when he had a motor cycle accident and sustained a broken neck. He was taken to the local hospital for immediate treatment and then transferred to a spinal injuries unit.

The resulting disability was very severe. James was completely paralysed below the level of his chest and this affected his bowel and bladder control. He has strong movement of his shoulders and upper arms, and some movement at his elbow and wrists, but his fingers are weak and he has poor grip. As he has loss of sensation below chest level, he is continually at risk from pressure or abrasions, particularly over his buttocks and his back.

James returned home to live with his parents after seven months in hospital, but he was very depressed and frustrated. While he was in the company of other young people in hospital the reality of his situation had not really dawned upon him, but now he was faced with being dependent to some degree on other people for the rest of his life, and the problems of living in a wheelchair. The possibility of working again seemed too remote even to discuss. His parents and brothers and sisters were very understanding and gave him every support and encouragement during his early depressive stage.

James tried to be independent for personal matters such as dressing, but found it very slow and exhausting, therefore his father used a portable hoist to get him up and into his wheelchair and to assist in his dressing and toilet. It was also used to hoist him into the family car so that he was able to get out and about.

A urinary appliance enabled him to cope well with his loss of bladder control, and the district nurse called three times a week to help with the bowel routine.

James' father obtained an electrically powered bed through the social services department so that James was able to control his sitting and laying positions by push button control, and this together with a sheepskin on his bed and in his wheelchair avoided unnecessary pressure on his body.

As time passed James has been able to adjust to his disability. He realised that he would never be able to return to his former employment as an apprentice toolmaker, and at the suggestion of his doctor, he started attending accountancy classes at the local polytechnic. His mother lifts him into the car with the hoist, and when he arrives he has many friends who help to lift him from the car to the wheelchair and help him around the building. He is once again enjoying the company of young people and the stimulus of study. He has written to his former employers asking if they would consider offering him a job in the clerical or accountancy field and has received a very encouraging reply.

His struggle towards a measure of independence has been long and arduous, but now that he has a real goal to work for all his efforts seem worthwhile.

Problem Solving Charts

EATING AND DRINKING PROBLEMS

Activity	Problem	Suggestions
Access to table	Close access to table in wheelchair	Desk arms on wheelchair. Dining-table of suitable height with sufficient clearance under for knees, and no obstructing cross-bars. Dining-table not too narrow, nor against wall, to accommodate footplates. Cantilever table. Tray table on wheelchair. Special tray on Monodrive etc.
Access for semi-ambulant	Stiff hips/knees	High dining-chair needed, correspondingly higher table. Tray on armchair.
	Reach	Reach in horizontal plane is assisted by having table at such a height that the elbows and forearms can rest on the table
	Stability	Where any ataxia or inco-ordination, or spasm, important that furniture is heavy and stable.

Activity	Problem	Suggestions
	Access to table when sitting in bed	Suitable back rest, giving stability and leaving arms free. Overbed table. Bed tray.
	Lying	When necessary to eat lying flat, plate can be balanced on chest or on bed trays. A bed mirror is then useful to see plate.
Ease of cleaning	Spilling food	Formica-topped table. Plastic tablecloth. P.V.C. upholstery on chairs. Plenty of paper napkins available. If bib is needed, it is unobtrusive if made of the same material as blouse/dress and backed with plastic foam and waterproof plastic material.
	Athetoid children	Plastic overall with sleeve or plastic bib and oversleeves with elastic cuffs.
Aids to arm/hand function		
Special table and accessories	Limited range of movement; table to mouth	Adjustable-height table, use elbow height for writing, raised for eating. Small box table, to required height stood on dining table, must be heavy based to give stability, or clip to table edge. Ditto with hole cut out for plate or bowl to drop in.
	Weakness of elbow muscles	An elbow ring pad suitably placed on

Activity	Problem	Suggestions
		table will give pivot point for elbows without risk of pressure-sore.
	Plate moving on a table	Important that plate is held still.
		Non-slip mats. Rubber suction pads ("Octopus"). Damp Wettex cloth. Dicem.
	Inco-ordination and tremor	Heavy plate, on mats (as above), or plate fitting into cut-out in tray or table, or suction pads fitted to base of bowl. Heavy china plates give more stability, but plastic does not break easily when dropped.
	Inability to catch food on plate	Ideally, plate with low rim at point of entry of spoon, and high rim on opposite side to push against, as Manoy Melaware.
		Clip-on plate buffer guard.
		Plate with deep rim, such as child's plate.
	Slowness in eating or swallowing	Specially-heated plate.
		Plate placed over soup plate of hot water.
	Arm and hand weakness	Lightweight plastic plates are easy to handle and can be stabilized on rubber mat.
	Egg cups	Suction-based egg-cups.
		Broad-based children's plastic egg-cups.
	Inability to pick up and grasp cutlery	Various handles to aid grasp to suit individual, such as built-up

Activity	Problem	Suggestions
		handles, using rubber, felt or plastic.
		Extended handle with grip over back of hand.
		Careful selection of cutlery on the market. Much stainless steel too clumsy, heavy and slippery.
		Avoid cutlery which lies flat to table, so difficult to pick up.
		A slight upward tilt at end of handle helps grasp.
		Select wooden handles well-shaped for grasp.
	Difficulty in bringing spoon to mouth at correct angle	Angled cutlery to suit individual. Some are available commercially or can be made with adjustable angle. Swivel spoon.
	Limited reach	Long-handled cutlery.
	Poor power in upper limb: spoon	Manoy Cutlery. A spork will catch food with less effort, but should not be used when there is any tremor—spoon only.
	Fork	Sharp prongs require less effort to spear with; 4-prong easier than Danish-type 3-prong.
	Knives	Steak knife with saw or serrated edge.
	One hand	Cheese knife, rather than clumsy and expensive Nelson knife. Fork with cutting edge, e.g. Eze eater or party forks.

Activity	*Problem*	*Suggestions*
Drinking	Inability to lift: from table	Use straws, clipped on to cup. Tipping-cup on stand. Plastic mug, softer type, picked up in teeth.
	in wheelchair	Drop-in holder for tumbler fixed to chair at shoulder-level, with straw.
	in bed	Cycle bottle carrier with long straw attached to bedside table.
	Difficulty in lifting without spilling	Children's training beakers, with round, weighted bottom.
	Weakness in grasp and lifting	Only half-fill cup, it is the liquid that weighs most. Choice of mugs, etc. on the market: lightweight ridged, e.g. Bex tumblers and mugs. Select cups with large handles. Two-handled plastic container for tumbler.
	Slowness—need to keep drink warm	Insulated plastic picnic mugs.
	Lack of sensation and risk of burning, e.g. tetraplegics who tend to balance cup on wrist or forearm, or hold between palmer surface both wrists	Insulated plastic mugs. Plastic containers.
	Disabled person on own during day time	Plastic stopper on thermos drilled, and plastic straw fitted. Drink will keep warm for several hours.

TOILET PROBLEMS

Activity	Problem	Suggestions
Access to toilet	General safety	Level access. Non-slip floors. Floor in good condition, i.e. no ragged lino or carpet edge. Good lighting in approach and in room. Grab-rails.
	Outside toilet	Level, non-slip access or ramp. Carport type weather protection.
	Housing: size of room	Reverse door to open outward. Fit sliding door. Review and when possible, remove all unessential furniture and fitting. If adjacent, remove part wall to make one room with bathroom.
	width of room	Use of narrow wheel-chair for toilet purpose only.
	steps	Two shallow steps preferable to one deep one. Grab-rail. Ramp for wheelchair (seldom practical indoors).
	Toilet: type	High or low cistern; high gives more transfer space, low sometimes useful to lean against. Corbel type allows closer approach.
	placing	Pedestal should preferably be at least 12 ins. (30 cms) from rear wall and 12 ins. (30 cms.) from the side-wall.

Activity	Problem	Suggestions
Transfering on/off	Height of toilet seat	Appropriate to individual most disabled are better suited with a seat height at 19 or 21 ins. (48 to 53 cms).
	Type of toilet seat	Old fashioned wooden bench-type preferable. Extension of bench, i.e. fixed sliding board to individual height. Horseshoe open front, easier for cleaning perineum, but may reduce stability. Back-rest may also be needed.
	Stiff hips	Seat higher at back than front.
	One stiff hip	Raised seat with cut-out for stiff hip. High box seat with arms at waist level to push up when rising and to lean on for balance when seated.
	Type of wheelchair	Aim is to minimize distance between toilet-seat and wheelchair: swinging detachable footrest; detachable arms; positive brakes; hard based cushion. Chairs with single cross brace allow very close approach forward to lavatory pan.
	Wheelchair cushions	Hard-based cushions aid transfer. Paraplegic cushion facilitates use of bottle or female urinal or small boat bedpan.
	Pulling up and balance: grab-rails	A horizontal grab-rail about 2 ft. 8 ins. (81 cms) from the ground and a vertical rail at a

Activity	Problem	Suggestions
		comfortable distance in front of the pedestal are usually found to be suitable. When balance poor, e.g. tetraplegic, side rail to lean on when seated. A bar which will drop down in front so that the patient can lean forward is sometimes preferred. Grab-rail in approach passage way may be necessary for semi-ambulant and also for pulling sani chair into room to go over W.C.
	Very stiff people or those with calipers tending to slide forward	Foot-stop on floor.
	Crutches, stick	Foolproof method of hanging or clipping them within easy reach (if dropped, the person may not be able to rise from toilet-seat).
	Methods of transfer: from wheelchair with good manoeuvrability	Individual's method of transfer adapted to space available. For wheelchair patients, an area of approximately 5 ft. × 5 ft. 9 ins. (160 × 180 cms) is often needed for toilet purposes. Others may manage in a space 2 ft. 9 ins. × 5 ft. 9 ins. (80 × 180 cms).
	from wheelchair in long narrow room	Approach facing pedestal and transfer forward, sitting facing wall.

Activity	Problem	Suggestions
		Low cistern is helpful to lean on.
	Too narrow for wheelchair	Transfer to commode chair at doorway, or outside door. If privacy allows, arrange clothes before transfer to commode chair.
		Use wooden chair as bridge chair standing inside door, should have non-slip rubber stops on feet of chair.
		Grab-rails outside may be necessary, especially where transfer method is to stand, pivot and then sit down.
Management of clothes	Limited reach (e.g. rheumatoid arthritis) women: pants down/up	Simple dressing-stick (need not be very long) to pull pants up/down. Wide-leg pants or split-pants; draw aside with dressing-stick to micturate.
		Tape loop sewn top of pants, loop over arm to prevent slipping down too far out of reach.
		No vest, wear thicker slip "princess" style; for warmth use brushed nylon slip, or cotton interlock.
		Wear waist-length top-let.
	skirt out of way	Raise skirt and slip together, draw towards front, roll and tuck into waist-band at front.

Activity	Problem	Suggestions
		Split back skirt and lining.
	suspenders	Back suspender moved to side of girdle so that one does not have to undo to sit on toilet seat.
Limited reach: men		
	trousers up/down	Wear braces, always loop over arm when lowering so that trousers do not fall to floor.
	pants up/down	Velcro into trousers, or tape loops on to braces.
	fly opening	Zip usually preferred; lengthen under crutch for wheelchair people. Toilet stick, if necessary, ring in zip pull-tag.
	tuck in shirt	Shorten back of shirt and use dressing stick. Wear overshirt.
	vest	Wear sleeveless pullover over shirt instead of vest.
One hand: women		Wide-leg or split pants (as above). Vest (as above). Suspender (as above). Pull up skirt and slip at back first, tuck in back of waist-band, then front. Dress, pull right up and take hem in teeth.
One hand: (man)		
	trouser/pants	As above.
	fly-opening	Buttons preferred.
	shirt-vest	As above.
	Paraplegic	Zip at lower inside seam of trousers for access to incontinence appliance.

Activity	Problem	Suggestions
		Cut-out at front of under-pants for access to incontinence appliance. If normal arms, no other problems.
	Wheelchair user with upper-limb weakness: women skirt	Split-back skirt and slip. Split pants with overlap. If in chair all day, no pants, sit on nappy.
	wheelchair with upper-limb weakness: men trousers up/down	Zip opening at both side-seams, and continuous front waistband.
Cleaning perineum	Fittings: toilet-paper	Paper placed within easy reach. Single sheets easier than roll for one hand.
	seat	"Horseshoe" seat, easier to clean self, especially for those with limited hip abduction.
	flush-handle	Flush-handle within reach. Pull-handle: lengthen chain and crankhandle to hang forward.
	washing	Portable bidet-spray in lavatory pan (shampoo spray) if in bathroom. Some disabled flush toilet while still seated on it. Closomat.
	Limited reach	Toilet stick—curved to suit individual, milled at end to hold paper.

Activity	Problem	Suggestions
		Tissue-type paper folds over and clings best. Wipe from front backward. Turn stick and tap against pan to drop paper.
Menstruation	Limited reach: weak hands; inability to cope with hygiene	Sanipants with tuck-in pads the easiest. For disabled women, it is much preferable to have lavatory in bathroom to facilitate washing perineum and hands, when necessary. Soak stained garments in cold water. Rinse with Savlon against odour.
Use of toilet at night	Outside toilet or toilet inaccessible	Commode beside bed. Right or left to suit individual.
	Urgency of micturition	Detachable arm of commode on bed side. Paper available.
	Poor balance Confusion	Adequate lighting.
	Cannot reach toilet without putting on calipers, etc.	Control of fluid intake—no drink after 8.00 p.m. Take bulk of fluids during morning.
	Emptying commode	Slide-out type easier than lift-out. Round steel easiest to keep clean. Use small trolley to carry, if necessary. If toilet is in bathroom, length of hose from hot tap to toilet is help in washing out commode pan.

Activity	Problem	Suggestions
		Leave a little Savlon in bottom of clean pan.
Incontinence	Micturition: men	Appropriate urinary appliance may be prescribed. Zip-opening on lower inside leg seam facilitates emptying bag. Tap enlarged when grip is impaired. Paraplegic cushion.
	Micturition: women	Urinary appliance seldom satisfactory. Paraplegic cushion with 'boat' bedpan, emptied frequently. Absorbent padding; protective pants.

BATHING PROBLEMS

Activity	Problem	Suggestions
Access to bath or shower	General safety	Level non-slip floor, etc. as for toilet. Non-slip bath-mat. Suitable grab-rails. Heated towel-rails must be low temperature.
	Housing: small bathroom; approach passage too narrow, with awkward turn in	Sliding-door as direct access from bedroom.
	Provision for over-head hoist	Check joists, or reinforce for over-head track. Consult electricity board for safety of electric hoist.
	Bath	Bath-side not blocked in, for approach of hoist or deep recess for wheelchair footplates.

157

Activity	Problem	Suggestions
	sufficient space to approach	Check manoeuvring space in bathroom for wheelchair.
	High rim to shower-pan	Transfer from chair placed outside shower-pan to seat inside.
		For ambulant people 2 or 3 shallow steps installed, up and over with ridged rubber surface and suitable grab-rail. When possible, instal shower with gently-sloping tiled floor and a floor drain, but no rim. This can be installed downstairs, but seldom upstairs.
Transfer to bath or shower	Height of bath	If transferring from wheelchair, the end of bath should be same height as chair or slightly lower.
		For those dependent on hoist to transfer, and helper to wash, then raise bath to convenient height for helper—but consider other members of the family, e.g. children.
		A safety non-slip mat in the bath is helpful in all cases.
	Type of bath	Bath should preferably have a flat bottom, e.g. Module bath.
		Shorter baths are often safer as the person cannot slip under water.
	Method from wheelchair to bath, side transfer	Close approach to bath—swinging detachable footrests. Positive brakes. Using overhead

Activity	*Problem*	*Suggestions*
		handle-grab, or rail on wall, place one or both legs over rim into bath, transfer to bath-rim, re-position legs, transfer down into bath.
	front approach to side of bath	Swinging detachable footrests. Positive brakes. Roll chair forward to side of bath, leave enough room to put one leg, then other over rim to bath. Release brakes; approach as close as possible, engage brake and using overhead hand-grip if necessary, transfer forward into bath. Using grab-rail on wall, if necessary turn in bath.
	front approach to end of bath	When space allows, technique as for front approach to side of bath but using the end of the bath, and also using overhead grab and/or grab-rail. Can be done with a wheelchair with fixed foot-rests, using a bench as a bridge, with foot-plates under it. This approach avoids having to turn in the bath.
	getting up out of bath	Get out before letting water out to gain some help from the water buoyancy. Sit on seat in bath (various types are available, e.g. toilet-seat type).

Activity	Problem	Suggestions
	Weak trunk, poor balance	Non-slip grab-rails must be fitted to suit the individual. May need helper for transfer, but once safe in bath may be able to wash self. Use a back rest in the bath. Wooden kitchen chair, or formed plastic garden chair, with legs cut down, stood in the bath. The chair must be stabilized by wood slats firmly over bath rim and crutch-tips on bottom of legs.
	Inco-ordination	Quick-release straps can be used to hold patient. Plastic bath-sling which hooks on side of bath is particularly useful for athetoid children.
	Unable to transfer without lifting equipment: hoists	Hoists on overhead rails can be fitted in small bathroom where a portable hoist is not practical. Simplest is track and trolley with bar handle-grip and can be used by one helper for the severely disabled such as tetraplegics. Hewitt Watson hoist with track and trolley. (N.B.—Special safety precautions are necessary when installing electric hoists in bathrooms.) Portable hoists such as

Activity	Problem	Suggestions
		New Oxford, Hoyer, Zimmer can be used in moderate-sized bathrooms, but require clear space under the bath for the legs of the hoist; minimum clearance is 9 ins. for most hoists, but check what is needed for newer models.
		Nylon net all-in-one bath slings are useful, and dry out easily.
		Back rest and/or head sling may be needed. Nylon strap-slings can be used and they scrub and dry easily.
	Transfers to bath: ambulant disabled	Seated side transfer from bathroom stool or extended bench is the best method for all elderly and semi-ambulant disabled.
	Shower in bath	Standing—shallow bath preferred.
		Vertical or ladder grab-rail.
		One or two steps up and over, with ridged rubber surface to steps.
		Bath seat or kitchen chair in bath.
		Use of hand shower.
		(N.B.—When vertical grab-bars are used they must have plastic or other non-slip winding. Wet hands slip very easily on smooth pole.)
	Transfer to shower:	A shower seat against wall and projecting beyond shower-curtain, acts as fixed slide-

Activity	Problem	Suggestions
		board and seat. Where a floor drain is installed and there is no rim to the shower-pan, glide about-type chair can be kept for taking showers, transferring from wheelchair by usual individual methods. A wooden kitchen chair, formed plastic chair or steel-framed canvas chair can be used.
		Special stools for amputees, or unilateral fixed hip can be made to individual need.
	grab-rails	Must suit individual need, but following will serve most disabled: Horizontal bar 3–4 ins. above wall side rim of bath, set out 3 ins. from wall; vertical bars, 2–3 ft. in length at either end of horizontal; 1½ ins. diameter; plastic winding or coating for non-slip grip.
Taps and fittings	Reaching taps: bath	Taps are more easily reached when fitted centre side rather than end of bath, but people often tend to use them to pull up. Lever-type taps can be fitted, or long-handled tap-turner used.
		Soap, brushes, face-cloths, etc. readily available either on shelf across bath, or basket hung on side.

Activity	*Problem*	*Suggestions*
	shower	A thermostat is essential for a shower used by disabled. Hand-operated shower hose, or same type in adjustable wallfitting preferred, not overhead rose. Tap within easy reach from shower-seat. Fitting for soap, brushes, etc. within easy reach.
Washing and drying	Washing, drying	Non-slip baby-soap. Bath-wrap towel on seat or wheelchair to wrap right round. Smaller towel or mitten towel for rubbing down. Best to rinse all soap from hands and if possible dry them before holding grab-rail to pull out.
	Unable to take bath or shower with family help available	District nurse can visit regularly to give person a bed bath when necessary, or to help family to bath person. Bath service often available when skilled nursing not needed. Ensures regular inspection without being too obvious, thus making sure that no scratches or bruises or any abnormalities are left to get so bad that hospitalization is required.

WASHING AND GROOMING PROBLEMS

Activity	Problem	Suggestions
Access to hand-basin	General (including safety)	Level access to hand-basin or other source of hot water. Non-slip floors; flooring in good condition. Good lighting. Appropriate grab-rails. Hot pipes lagged. Low-heat towel rail. Warm room. Privacy. Stable bathroom stool.
	Housing: width of door	As for toilet. 2 ft. 3 ins. minimum.
	steps	No step or threshold rim at entrance.
	handbasin	Height to suit individual, approximately 32 ins. for wheel-chair; 36 ins. standing.
	type	Non-pedestal type, access for wheelchair. Support at side, if necessary, leaving clear knee-room. Waste-pipe insulated. Any sharp edges, e.g. nut on waste-trap covered to avoid abrasion of knees. Helpful to have shelf fitted up to side of handbasin to lean elbows on and to keep accessories to hand. Mirror above basin larger than average so that seated disabled and standing family can both use. For some patients, it is helpful to be able to

Activity	*Problem*	*Suggestions*
		wash while seated on toilet.
	placing	May be necessary to stand basin out from wall to accommodate wheelchair footplates, and stiff calipered legs if seated on stool to wash.
	Unable to use hand-basin or difficult access to bathroom	Plastic bowl on lap-board or low table or chair, though help may be needed to carry and fill bowl; disabled person can get on washing while helper does other chores.
		Plastic bowl in cut-out in shelf/table, cannot tip and is support for elbows.
Ability to reach	Stiff shoulders, elbows, trunk	Consider method before aids e.g. support forearms on shelf.
		May be easier to wash perineum whiles eated on toilet.
		Long-handled sponge, comb, safety razor, etc. made to individual need, e.g. enlarged handle, handle curved to grip back of hand, friction grip surface.
		All accessories, soap, face-cloth, shaving tackle, etc. kept within close range and reach.
	Drying	Dry terry towelling is probably the best; if possible it should be warmed before use, and then it will dry without rubbing. It

Activity	Problem	Suggestions
		may help to have one end of towel firmly fixed to towel rail. Most disabled have difficulty handling a large towel, two small ones are better. Mitten-end towels made from roller-type terry towelling (like oven cloth), helpful for weak grip.
	Stiff hips, knees	Some disabled can wash and dry feet at long range, using aids, e.g. long-handled bath-brush. May need help, but this can be minimal if bowl with hot soapy water put for feet to soak, lift out on to hot terry towel.
		Need help caring for toenails regularly (chiropody service).
Ability to grip	Weak, painful hands: washing	Terry towelling mitten may be easier than face-cloth. Wide tape sewn over back of sponge—slip hand through. Pimple rubber, curved handles on aids to suit individual. Nailbrush suction to handbasin.
	teeth	Soak dentures. Toothbrush with adapted handle, if necessary. Suitable plastic mug (2-handled; non-tip). For inco-ordination or tremor, or weak arms, rest both elbows on shelf, hold brush in

Activity	*Problem*	*Suggestions*
		right hand, grip right wrist with left hand then move head rather than hand to brush round mouth.
		Electric tooth-brush.
	shaving	Electric razor with clip-on double hand grip. Electric-razor stand with stiffish ball-and-socket joint. Move face over razor.
Care of nails	Hands	Filing is much safer than cutting or clipping, especially when any inco-ordination or loss of sensation is present. File suitably fixed to dressing table or with enlarged handle.
		Nails best kept short, to avoid snagging and breaking during transfers and to avoid abrasions to the skin.
		If difficulty is experienced in cleaning the nails, soak well in hot, soapy water and rub against piece of terry towelling in bottom of bowl.
	Feet	If patient cannot safely reach feet and cut nails, it is better not to attempt to use aids; will probably need regular help in washing and it is best to have regular help with toe-nails. There is usually health department provision for chiropody if bunions, corns or in-

Activity	*Problem*	*Suggestions*
		growing nails need attention.
Care of hair	Style	Short hair style preferable, easier to wash, can be brushed often. A perm is not necessarily helpful, for unless the hair is well set after washing, it can friz and look worse than a straight simple style.
	Washing hair	Wash with hair-sprayer on taps. Care of scalp and prevention of dandruff by washing frequently with special shampoo after application of scalp lotion. Wash, brush and comb whenever hair is washed.
Care of skin	Dry skin	Many disabled tend to have dry scaly skin, especially on legs and feet. Savlon baths are useful. Soak feet in warm soapy water. Dry well but carefully, as skin is often thin and brittle from prolonged inactivity and poor circulation. Massage with oil (arachis oil more readily available and cheaper than olive oil) or use calamine cream as an alternative.
	Pressure areas	Especially buttocks when chair-bound. Sit and sleep on sheepskin. Regular inspection of skin; patient can check by using hand mirror.

Activity	Problem	Suggestions
		Wash every day, dry very well, either with rolling movement on bed or chair doing one side at a time sitting on towel.
		Dust lightly with talcum powder.
		Folds of buttocks and in groins are better with oily ointment such as zinc cream or a barrier cream rubbed in sparingly.

COMMUNICATION PROBLEMS

Activity	Problem	Suggestions
Spoken word	Reception, hard of hearing: deafness	Visual: lip-reading, written word; pictures and signs. See Royal Institute for the Deaf publications.
	Speech, respiratory complications; lack of volume, etc. (e.g. Parkinsonism) lack of contact beyond immediate environment	Alphabet and sign-board writing. Speech amplifier. Adapted telephone (see G.P.O. pamphlet). Remote-control system (e.g. Possum). Intercom call systems. Remote-control door answer and opener. Call-bell and call lights.
	loss of speech from dyaphasias.	Speech therapy. Follow-up practice.
Written word, reading	Partially sighted, blindness.	Magnifiers. Large-print books. Braille, tape recorders, talking books.

Activity	Problem	Suggestions
		See Royal National Institute for the Blind publications.
	Inability to handle books and papers	Simple aids: rubber thimble, paper clips, etc. Reading stands and newspaper racks. Mechanical page-turners.
Writing	Dyslexia	Speech therapy. Follow-up practice.
	General:	Suitable tables: surface, height, tilting wheelchair table.
	inability to hold pencil and paper	Simple aids: penholder, clip-board, magnet board, Splints, e.g. flexorhinge splints.
	loss of arm function	Mobile arm-supports. Slings.
	amputee	Prostheses: conventional; powered. Use of feet and mouth
	Cerebral dysfunction: agraphia	Speech therapy. Follow-up practice.
Typing	Slight loss of function in arm and hand: Inco-ordination	Keyguard. Simple aids: weighted cuff; non-slip mat.
	Severe loss of function in arms and hands	Mobile arm-supports. Electric typewriter. Continuous-fold paper. Aids for feeding-in paper.
	Total loss of function arms and hands	Mouthstick; headstick.

CLOTHING PROBLEMS

Disability	Problem	Suggestions
Cardiacs and Bronchitics	Elderly people. At their worst in morning Need to conserve energy Liable to giddiness	Choice of clothing. Reduce number of garments worn. Avoid heavy clothes. Front-opening fastenings are easier to manage. Method. Plenty of time and privacy needed to avoid worry. Carry out most of routine seated; avoid bending down to put on socks/stockings/shoes and trousers, lift foot onto chair. Adaptations—not necessary.
Hemiplegia	May be: Confusion Loss of balance Loss of spatial sense Easily flustered One-handed	Choice of clothing. As simple as possible. Stretch fabrics are easier to pull on and off. Easy front-fastenings which can be managed with one hand. Women: Pullfront corset with either Velcro fastening or sliding bar buckle. Front fastening bra with adapted fastening if necessary. Open crotch pants are helpful for toileting. Method. Prolonged training in simple routine in a quiet unhurried atmosphere. Teach only one process

Disability	Problem	Suggestions
		at a time starting with managing clothes for toilet.
		Place everything needed during dressing and undressing on un-affected side (likeli-hood of falling to the paralysed side).
		Start independent dres-sing on bed, progres-sing to sitting on side of bed with support avail-able on affected side, or sitting on a stable chair at side of bed. A table in front of the person to take the weight of the clothes may be helpful.
		Braces can be used to pull trousers up and prevent their dropping down during toileting.
		Stand with support for final arrangement of clothes.
		Avoid bending with the head down. Put socks/stockings/shoes on by placing foot of af-fected side on a stool or across opposite knee.
		Adaptations.
		Women:
		Re-position back sus-penders well forward to side of corset.
		Alternatively, suspen-ders can be fixed to stockings and hooked onto corset.
		Adapted split pants for toileting if ready made not available.

Disability	Problem	Suggestions
		Men: Underpants can be attached to trousers by Velcro or by braces. Aids are best avoided, simple routine preferable.
Rheumatoid arthritis	Pain and stiffness most severe in the morning	Choice of clothing Light, warm, loose clothes.
	Limitations of movement	Raglan sleeves are easier to put on and off.
	Joint deformities	Clothes which can be put on over head are usually easier than coat style ones
	Difficulty in standing and therefore in dressing lower half as well as upper half	**Women:** Front-fastening bra adapted if necessary or a Lycra stretch bra with back-fastening sewn up may be sufficient support for a small woman.
	Weak grip	Pullfront corset with either Velcro or pull-through fastening or an all-in-one liberty bodice type of corset.
		Men: Overshirt easier to put on than jacket style shirt.
		To overcome limited internal rotation of shoulder, a T shirt, which does not require tucking in, can replace a vest.
		Method. Sitting position may be easier for dressing. Generally, clothes which can be put on

Disability	Problem	Suggestions
		over the head are easier than coat style. A table in front of patient to support elbows when putting clothes over head may be helpful. Adaptations. Easy fastenings, e.g. Velcro dabs. Slippery linings fitted in cardigans or other garments which stick, make them easier to put on and off. Women: Adapted front-fastening to bra if necessary. Men: Underpants attached to trousers by Velcro. Simple aids. Lightweight dressing stick. Long-handled shoe horn. Spring steel button hook. Pick-up skick. Stocking gutter. Sock gutter.
Hip disabilities	Difficulty in reaching to feet, in putting on socks/ stockings/shoes and pulling clothes up to waist Caliper may be worn	Choice of clothing. Wide leg trousers or full skirts are necessary for easier dressing if calipers are worn. Women: Cami-knickers with gusset-opening or open crotch pants may be helpful for toileting. Tights may be preferred to stockings because of the difficulty

Disability	*Problem*	*Suggestions*
		of obtaining comfortable corsetry and attaching suspenders.
		Method.
		Caliper wearer:
		Must not stand without caliper; socks/ stockings/shoes and caliper must be put on lying on bed. Elderly people will probably require help.
		No caliper:
		Socks/stockings/shoes can be put on sitting on side of bed using a stocking aid, shoe horn or long-handled reacher.
		Women:
		Cami-knickers and skirts can be put on over the head, pulled down and adjusted while standing. A placket opening can be lengthened if necessary.
		Adaptations.
		Caliper wearer.
		Zip inserted into inner leg seam from ankle to knee opening from the bottom up enables trousers to be put on over caliper more easily.
		Shoe laces can be done up with a dressing stick or elastic laces can be used. One side of the top of the shoe tongue should be stitched to the shoe's upper.
		Women:
		Adapted split pants are

Disability	Problem	Suggestions
		helpful for toileting. Simple aids. Long-handled shoe-horn. Stocking/sock aid. Long-handled reacher. Dressing stick.
Paraplegia	Spasm Skin breakdown Incontinence	Choice of clothing. For wheelchair use a cape, poncho or short coat is more comfortable than a full-length coat. Smooth-fitting stretch socks which should not be tight nor have elastic tops prevent wrinkles inside shoes. Plastic sleeves protect cuffs and keep them clean. Leather reinforcements on inner side of jacket sleeves protect from wear and tear on propelling wheels of chair. Women: Two-piece dresses are easily tidied and do not ride up. Special waterproof pants and disposable pads may be necessary. Method. Dress lower half on bed for safety if there is spasm. If no spasm, dressing can be carried out in the wheelchair. Adaptations. A zip inserted into lower seam of trouser leg opening from bot-

Disability	Problem	Suggestions
		tom upwards is easier both for dressing and emptying of urine bag.
Tetraplegia	Inadequate sitting balance Spasm Skin breakdown Incontinence Excessive sweating Loss of hand grip	Choice of clothing. Loose lightweight clothing with raglan sleeves. Cotton underwear which absorbs moisture and can be boiled. If aim is independent dressing, avoid clothes which have to be pulled over the head as sight is necessary to maintain balance. For wheelchair use, a cape, poncho, or short coat is more comfortable than a full-length coat. Women: Wrap-round skirt with half-length slip attached is easier to put on; slacks which are warmer and more convenient for transfer may be preferred and eliminate the need for stockings and suspenders. Tights with crotch-opening are convenient for toilet purposes. Special waterproof pants and disposable pads may be necessary. A woman who has difficulty in managing pants and is without help during the day may prefer to dispense with pants and sit on a soft absorbent towel.

Disability	Problem	Suggestions
		Method. Most tetraplegics will require help in dressing their lower half, and with putting on corset or braces. Lower half most easily dressed with person sitting on bed supported by a backrest leaving both hands free. Clothes above waist can be put on sitting in wheelchair with table in front to support elbows. A quick-release restraining strap may be needed across knees if leg spasm likely to throw person off balance. Adaptations. Tape loops sewn into garments enable finger or thumb to be hooked into loop for pulling garment where handgrip is impaired. Velcro dabs to replace buttons. A zip inserted into lower inner seam of trouser leg opening from button upwards is easier both for dressing and emptying of urine bag. Simple aids. Rubber stationery thimbles on index fingers help to grip material. Spring steel button hook. Dressing hook

Disability	Problem	Suggestions
Inco-ordination	Cerebral Palsy Unwanted movement Complete dressing independence may be attained with repeated practice and persistence in a calm atmosphere	Choice of clothing. Loose-fitting clothes of stretch materials which can be put on over the head are preferable to jacket style. Raglan sleeves are preferable to insert sleeves. Fastenings should be avoided. Zips are difficult to manage and Velcro may not stand up to continuous pull of athetoid movements. Buttons on strong elastic or tape shanks are preferable. Firm, lace-up shoes with toe reinforcement. Probably need help in tying shoelaces. Method. Must be individually arranged. Adaptations. Openings should be reinforced with tape or extra machine stitching. The tongue of the shoe must be sewn firmly to the upper at one side to keep it in place while foot is pushed into shoe.
Upper limb amputees	Through shoulder amputees may need help in putting on their prostheses Other amputees will be able to put on prostheses themselves	Choice of clothing. Loose-fitting clothes permit operation of prosthesis without hindrance. Garments should be of hard-wearing fabric to withstand friction.

Disability	Problem	Suggestions
	Single upper limb amputees will have little difficulty in dressing though the through shoulder amputee will require practice	A vest worn under the harness prevents rubbing of the skin. Overshirts or blouses eliminate the need to tuck clothes into trousers.
	Fastenings to centre line of body are difficult for above-elbow amputees	Method. When putting on a long-sleeved garment prosthesis is put into sleeve first and pulled well up the arm.
	Double arm amputees will have considerable difficulties	One-handed methods for tying shoelaces and tie should be taught. Adaptations.
	Bilateral above-elbow amputees will need some help	Zip with large ring-pull on front trouser fastenings may be managed with short curved dressing stick. Simple aids. Short curved dressing stick.
Lower limb amputees	Should be able to dress and undress independently but elderly people may find it a tiring and slow process	Choice of clothing. Loose-fitting clothes of hard-wearing fabric. Thick stockings wear better than thin ones and conceal the prosthesis, but trousers may be preferred. Waist bands may need to be a size larger to fit over the prosthesis harness. Right size of stump sock. A thick undersock should be used on the artificial foot. Shoe on artificial foot should have a flexible sole.

Disability	Problem	Suggestions
		Women with above-knee amputations should not vary height of their shoe heel without reference to limb-fitting centre as this may affect the alignment and stability of the limb.

Method.
There must be no creases or folds in the stump sock.
Some people with one artificial limb may prefer to dress the limb with pants, trousers and shoe before fitting it onto the stump and before dressing the sound leg.
Others may prefer to put the shoe on last to prevent passing a dirty shoe through the clothes.
Bilateral lower limb amputees dress both artificial limbs completely before fitting them onto the stumps.
Adaptations.
Women:
Stockings can be protected with stocking guards which must be fitted at the limb-fitting centre.
Men:

Disability	Problem	Suggestions
Lower limb amputees		Trousers may need protection from damage by the artificial limb. A clothing pad of leather can be fixed to back of thigh piece by the limb maker, or people can insert a lining into back of trouser leg.

These suggestions are based on *Management of the Severely Disabled by* P. J. R. Nichols, and used by kind permission of the publishers, Butterworths, London.

Sources of Information

Abbeyfield Society, 23 Nottingham Place, London W1.

Access for the Disabled, 34 Eccleston Square, London SW1.

Access to University and Polytechnic Buildings, Central Council for the Disabled, 34 Eccleston Square, London SW1.

Age Concern (formerly National Old People's Welfare Council), 55 Gower Street, London WC1.

Association for Spina Bifida and Hydrocephalus Ltd., 112 City Road, London EC1.

Association of Occupational Therapists, 251 Brompton Road, London SW3.

"Break" Children's Holiday Schemes, 100 First Avenue, Bush Hill Park, Enfield, Middx.

British Association for the Hard of Hearing, Hon. Sec. Syke Ings, Iver, Bucks.

British Council for Rehabilitation of the Disabled, Tavistock House (South), Tavistock Square, London WC1.

British Epilepsy Association, 3–6 Alfred Place, London WC1.

British Heart Foundation Appeal, 57 Gloucester Place, London W.

British Institute for the Achievement of Human Potential, Bridge Hall, Rickerscote Road, Stafford.

British Polio Fellowship, Clifton House, 83/117 Euston Road, London NW1.

British Red Cross Society, 14 Grosvenor Crescent, London SW1.

British Rheumatism and Arthritis Association, 1 Devonshire Place, London W1N 2BD.

British Society for Music Therapy, 48 Lancaster Road, London N6.

British Talking Book Service for the Blind, 224 Great Portland Street, London W1N 6AA.

British Toy Council, Regent House, 89 Kingsway, London WC2.

British Wireless Fund for the Blind, 224 Great Portland Street, London W1N 6AA.

Brittle Bone Society, Secretary, Mrs. Margaret Grant, 63 Byron Crescent, Dundee.

Central Council for the Disabled, 34 Eccleston Square, London SW1.

Centre of Environment for the Handicapped, 24 Nutford Place, London W1H 6AN.

Chartered Society of Physiotherapy, Tavistock House, Tavistock Square, London WC1.

Chest and Heart Association, Tavistock House (North), Tavistock Square, London WC1.

Church Army, 185 Marylebone Road, London NW1.

Citizen's Advice Bureau, National Head Office, 26 Bedford Square, London WC1.

Citizen's Rights Office, 1 Macklin Street, Drury Lane, London WC2B 5NH.

College of Speech Therapists, 47 St. John's Wood, High Street, London NW8.

Community Service Volunteers, 237 Pentonville Road, London N1.

Cystic Fibrosis Research Trust, Stuart House, 1 Tudor Street, London EC4.

Department of Education and Science, Curzon Street, London W1.

Department of Health and Social Security, Alexander Fleming House, London SE1.

Director of Social Services (City Hall or Town Hall of nearest large town) for re-direction if necessary.

Disabled Drivers' Association, Ashwellthrope Hall, Ashwellthrope, Norwich.

Disablement Income Group, Godalming, Surrey.

Disabled Living Foundation, 346 Kensington High Street, London W14.

Domiciliary Occupational Therapy Service (City Hall or Town Hall of nearest large town) for re-direction if necessary.

Duke of Edinburgh's Award Scheme, 2 Old Queen Street, London SW1.

Elizabeth Fitzroy Homes for the Handicapped Trust, Miss E. Fitzroy, The Welfare Department, The Coach House, Whitegates, Liss, Hants.

Equipment for the Disabled, National Fund for Research into Crippling Diseases, Horsham, Sussex.

Girl Guides Association, 17 Buckingham Palace Road, London SW1.

Greater London Association for the Disabled, 183 Queensway, London W2.

Guides for the Disabled, Automobile Association, Fanum House, Stanmore, Middx.

Haemophilia Society, 16 Trinity Street, London SE1.

Holiday Information Service for the Physically Handicapped, Central Council for the Disabled, 34 Eccleston Square, London SW1.

Homebound Craftsmen's Shop, 25a Holland Street, London W8.

Hospital Centre, 24 Nutford Place, London W1H 6AN.
Information Service for the Disabled, Horsham, Sussex.
Invalid Children's Aid Association, 126 Buckingham Palace Road, London SW1.
Invalids-at-Home, 23 Farm Avenue, London NW2.
Joint Committee on Mobility for the Disabled, c/o The Spastics Society, 12 Park Crescent, London W1.
Lady Hoare Trust for Thalidomide and other physically disabled Children, 78 Hamilton Terrace, London NW8.
Limbless Swimmers (Adventure Club and Holiday Centre), Mr. V. Sims, 30 Palmer Road, Whitnash, Leamington Spa.
Multiple Sclerosis Society, 4 Tachbrook Street, London SW1.
Muscular Dystrophy Group, 26 Borough High Street, London SE1, and, Newcastle General Hospital, Westgate Road, Newcastle upon Tyne.
National Association of Boys' Clubs, 17 Bedford Square, London SW1.
National Association for Deaf, Blind and Rubella Children, 61 Sennelys Park Road, Northfield, Birmingham 31.
National Association of Youth Clubs, 30 Devonshire Street, London W1.
National Council of Social Service, 26 Bedford Square, London WC1.
National Federation of Housing Societies, 86 The Strand, London WC2.
National Fund for Research into Crippling Diseases, Horsham, Sussex.
National League for the Blind and Disabled, T. S. Parker, 262 Langham Road, London N15.
National Library for the Blind, 35 Great Smith Street, London SW1.
National Old People's Welfare Council, 26 Bedford Square, London WC1.
National Playing Fields Association, Register of Adventure Playgrounds for the Handicapped, 57b Catherine Place, London SW1.
Opportunity Class for handicapped children (pre-school age), Dr. R. E. Faulkner, 66 High Street, Stevenage, Herts.
P.O.S.M. Project Research, 63 Mandeville Road, Aylesbury.
Queen Elizabeth Foundation for the Disabled, Leatherhead Court, Leatherhead, Surrey.
Riding for the Disabled Association, National Equestrian Centre, Kenilworth, Warks.
Royal National Institute for the Blind, 224 Great Portland Street, London W1.
Royal National Institute for the Deaf, 105 Gower Street, London WC1.

Royal Society for the Prevention of Accidents, 52 Grosvenor Gardens, London SW1.

Scout Association, 25 Buckingham Palace Road, London SW1.

Society of Chiropodists, 8 Wimpole Street, London W1.

Social Services Department (addresses of local departments available from Town Hall or local libraries).

Spastics Society, 12 Park Crescent, London W1, and, 16 Fitzroy Square, London W1P 5HQ.

St. John Ambulance Brigade, 8 Grosvenor Crescent, London SW1.

Toc H Inc., 15 Trinity Square, London EC3N 4DI.

Toy Libraries Association, Mrs. J. Morris, 21 Gentleman's Row, Enfield, Middx.

Ulverscroft Large Print Books, F. A. Thorpe Publishing Ltd., Station Road, Glenfield, Leicester.

Winged Fellowship Trust, Holiday Homes for the Physically Handicapped (over 15 years). Mrs. Brander, 79 Petty France, London SW1.

Wingfield Music Club, General Secretary, Mr. B. J. Cook, 24 Station Road, Epping, Essex.

Wishing Well Holiday Homes, Baden-Powell Scout Guild Holiday Home Trust, 25 Buckingham Palace Road, London SW1W 0PY.

Women's Royal Voluntary Service, 17 Old Park Lane, London W1Y 4A.

Youth Services Information Centre, 37 Belvoir Street, Leicester LE1 6SL.

Further Reading

Access to Public Conveniences, A handbook for the disabled person (Central Council for the Disabled, London)

Aids for the Disabled—illustrated catalogue (British Red Cross Society, 1968)

Around the Clock Aids for the Child with Muscular Dystrophy (Muscular Dystrophy Associations of America Inc., 1790 Broadway, New York 19, U.S.A.)

Cornell, M., *Early Days—you and your new baby* (Disabled Living Foundation, 1973)

Davis, W. M., *Self Aids* (Thistle Foundation, 1970)

Disabled User: Research Institute for Consumer Affairs Comparative Tests Reports:
  1. Refrigerators; 2. Reading Aids: Page Turners; 3. Reading Aids: Microfilm Projectors; 4. Reading Aids: Prismatic Spectacles; 5. Cookers; 6. Easy Chairs; 7. Gas fires; 8. Pick-up Sticks; 9. Can Openers; 10. Vacuum cleaners; 11. Bed/Chair Tables; 12. Foodmixers; 13. Bath Aids (National Fund for Research into Crippling Diseases, Horsham)

Equipment for the Disabled, 3rd Edition: 1. Wheelchairs and Outdoor Transport; 2. Communication; 3. Home Management; 4. Clothing and dressing; 5. Personal care; 6. Gardening and Leisure; 7. Housing and Furniture; 8. Hoists and Walking aids; 9. The Disabled Child; 10. The Disabled Mother. (National Fund for Research and Crippling Disease)

Equipment for the Physically Handicapped (The Spastics Society, 1968)

Elphick, L., *Incontinence* (Disabled Living Foundation, 1970)

Finnie, N. R., *Handling the young cerebral palsied child at home* (Heineman Medical Book, 1968)

Greaves, M., *Work and Disability* (British Council for Rehabilitation of the Disabled, 1969)

Hyams, D., *The Care of the Aged* (Priory Press, 1973)

Jay, P. E., Walker, E., and Ellison, A., *Help Yourself, a handbook for Hemiplegics and their families* (Butterworths, 1966)

Home Made Aids for the Disabled (British Red Cross Society, revised 1969)

Kitchen Equipment (Disabled Living Foundation)

Marriage, Sex and Arthritis (The Arthritis and Rheumatism Council)

MacCartney, P., *Clothes Sense for the handicapped adult of all ages* (Disabled Living Foundation)

Still at Home with Multiple Sclerosis (Multiple Sclerosis Society of Great Britain and Northern Ireland, 1972)

Verboven, L., *The Toy—a new therapeutic aid* (British Toy Council, 1966)

White, A. S., *The Easy Path to Gardening* (Readers Digest Association, London)

Your Child with Spina Bifida, a practical guide for parents; Your Child with Hydrocephalus, a practical guide for parents (Association for Spina Bifida and Hydrocephalus)

Index